Scottish Folk & Fairy Tales

Selected and Edited by
Sir George Douglas

LOMOND

This edition published by
Lomond Books 2005

This edition first published by Parragon

Parragon
Queen Street House
4 Queen Street
Bath BA1 1HE, UK

Produced by Magpie Books, an imprint of
Constable & Robinson Ltd, London.

Copyright in this setting © Parragon 2003

This collection first published c. 1892 by the
Walter Scott Publishing Company, London.

A copy of the British Library Cataloguing-in-Publication Data
is available from the British Library.

ISBN 1-84204-064-2

Printed and bound in UK

Acknowledgements

The publishers would like to thank Duff Burrell for his kind permission to use this collection.

Contents

Giants and Monsters

Legends and Traditions

Fairy Tales

The Brownie, the Bogle, the Kelpy, Mermen, Demons

Witchcraft

Contents

Literary Tales

Introduction

It is only within comparatively recent years that the homely stories in the mouths of the country-people have been constituted a branch of learning, and have had applied to them, as such, the methods and the terminology of science. No doubt a very noteworthy gain to knowledge has resulted from this treatment: a curious department of research has been opened up, and light has been cast upon various outside things of greater importance than the subject of study itself. But, side by side with this gain to knowledge, is there not, involved in the method of treatment indicated, a loss to the stories themselves? Classified, tabulated, scientifically named, they are no longer the wild free product of Nature that we knew and loved: they are become, so to speak, a collection of butterflies in a case, an album of pressed wild flowers. No doubt they are still very interesting, and highly instructive; but their poetry, their brightness, the fragrance which clung about them in their native air, their native soil, is in large measure gone! Well then – with all due recognition of the value of the labours of the scientific folk-lorist, the comparative mythologist, whose work I would not for one moment be understood to undervalue – is there not room, even at the present day, to study these stories from another point of view, and that the simplest and most obvious one – the point of view, I mean, of the *story-teller* pure and simple? One would hope that the time had not yet come when the old tales, considered on their own merits, have entirely ceased to charm; and it is an undeniable fact that there are still persons among us who would regard it as a real and personal loss could they be made to believe that the ideal hero of their childhood, as he falls heroically, in a bloody battle, wounded to the death, is in reality a myth, or an allegory to embody the setting of the sun; and who would even feel themselves aggrieved could they be brought to realise that the bugbear of their baby years – their own particular bugbear – is common also to the aborigines of Polynesia. So great is the power of early association. Well then, my proposal is to consider the Tales of the Scottish Peasantry simply from the literary, critical, or story-teller's point of view; from the point of view, that is, of persons who actually tell them, to whom they are actually told.

I suppose that most nations, whilst their life has remained primitive, have practised the art of story-telling; and certainly the Scotch were no exceptions to the rule. Campbell of Isla, who wrote about thirty years ago, records that in his day the practice of story-telling still lingered in the remote Western Islands of Barra; where, in the long winter nights, the people would gather in crowds to listen to those whom they considered good exponents of the art. At an earlier date – but still, at that time, within living memory – the custom survived at Poolewe in Ross-shire; where the young people were used to assemble at night to hear the old ones recite the tales which they had learned from their fore-fathers. Here, and at earlier dates in other parts of the country also, the demand for stories would further be supplied by travelling pedlars, or by gaberlunzie men, or pauper wandering musicians and entertainers, or by the itinerant shoemaker or tailor – 'Whip-the-Cat' as he was nicknamed – both of which last were accustomed to travel through thinly-populated country districts, in the pursuit of their calling, and to put up for the night at farm-houses – where, whilst plying their needles, they would entertain the company with stories.

The arrival of one of these story-tellers in a village was an important event. As soon as it became known, there would be a rush to the house where he was lodged, and every available seat – on bench, table, bed, beam, or the floor – would quickly be appropriated. And then, for hours together – just like some first-rate actor on a stage – the story-teller would hold his audience spell-bound. During his recitals, the emotions of the reciter were occasionally very strongly excited, as were also those of his listeners, who at one time would be on the verge of tears, at another would give way to loud laughter. There were many of these listeners, by the way, who believed firmly in all the extravagances narrated. And such rustic scenes as these, as I hope presently to show, have by no means been without their marked effect upon Scottish literature.

In his tour through the Islands, Campbell of Isla – my auhority for these particulars – visited one of the old story-tellers in his home. The man was far advanced in years, and he lived in a rude hut on the shore at South Uist. Campbell describes the scene in detail. The hut consisted of one room only. The fireplace was the floor, and the chimney a hole above it, so that the air was dense with peat-smoke, whilst the rafters were hung with streamers and festoons of soot. The old man himself had the manner of a practised narrator – he would chuckle at certain places in his story, and, like an Ancient Mariner or like one of the Weird Sisters, would lay a withered finger on the listener's knee when he came to the terrifying parts. A little boy in a kilt stood at his knee, gazing in his wrinkled face, and devouring every word. Whilst the story lasted, three wayfarers dropped in, listened for a while, and then proceeded on their way. The daylight streamed down the chimney, lighting up a tract in the blue mist of the peat-smoke and falling on the white hair and brown wrinkled face of the old man, as he sat on a low stool by the fire, and on the rest of the dwelling, with its furniture of boxes and box-beds, dresser, dishes, gear of all sorts – until at last it faded away, through shades of deepening brown, to the black darkness of the smoked roof and the corner where the peat was stored.

To turn now from the story-teller to the stories. Perhaps the most characteristic of the Highland tales are those – somewhat tedious they are, it must he confessed, with all their repetitions of dialogues, all their reproductions of what is practically one situation – which deal with heroes and giants. The shortest kind of popular tale, on the other hand, is that which is concerned with the dumb animals – by no means dumb, of course, in the stories. The Highlands, too, are particularly rich in these tales; and it is easy to understand how the country-people generally – living so near to nature as they do – may come to have an insight into, and an appreciation of, the character of the brute animals, together with a sympathy with them in their tussle for existence, which is not attainable by those who lead a more artificial life. Some of the apologues and traits of animal life in which this knowledge and appreciative sympathy have been embodied are decidedly naive and quaint. Nor do they lack a pungent human application.

The class of stories next to be considered displays a higher degree of fancy. And it must not be imagined that this quality of fancy is anything less than a characteristic attribute of the minds of many of the Scotch peasantry. It displays itself in its simplest form perhaps in their nomenclature in the names which they have given either to natural objects, or to places which are characterised by some striking natural feature. In the Highlands, the Gaelic place-names are often very elaborate indeed; but to turn now to the Lowlands. A waterfall in the Selkirkshire hills, where the water, after pouring dark over a declivity, dashes down in white foam among rocks, is known as The Grey Mare's Tail; twin hills in Roxburghshire, which have beautifully rounded matched summits, have been christened Maiden's Paps. Then, the cirrus, or curl-cloud, is in rustic speech, 'goat's hair'; the phenomenon of the Northern Lights, among the fishermen of Shetland, is the 'Merry Dancers'; the Pleiades are the 'Twinklers'; the constellation of Orion, with its star *iota* pendant as if from a girdle, is the 'King's Ellwand', or yard-measure; the noxious froth which adheres to the stalks of rank vegetation at midsummer is the 'Witches' spittle'. There is a root of poetry, I think, in this aptitude for giving names; and, as a matter of fact, in the Lowlands of Scotland, rustic poets and rhymesters are far from uncommon. Nor are the peasantry, in their name-giving, wanting in literary allusiveness – allusiveness, that is, to the only book which has ever obtained universal currency among them. For example, among the fishermen of the East Coast, the black mark below the gills of a haddock is 'Peter's Thumb'; whilst a coarse plant commonly found in corn-fields, which has its leaves strangely clouded and stained as if with droppings, and is called, I believe, by the botanists, *Polygonum persicaria,* is locally known on the Borders as 'The Flower which grew at the Foot of the Cross'.

Perhaps the deepest thinkers among a people who have their philosophers as well as their dreamers, are to be found among the hill shepherds. And it is chiefly through the instrumentality of one of these hill shepherds that we can now, in fancy, enter that realm of fancy, the world of Fairyland. James Hogg, the Ettrick Shepherd, was one of those common men, *plus* genius, who every now and then in the history of literature give to a whole world of floating thought, fancy, tradition, a permanent substantial form. No man in literature is his master in the weird tale. No man, but Shakespeare – not even excepting Drayton – has written so well of the fairies.

Hogg was born in the Arcadia of Scotland, Ettrick Forest, where, as Scott tells us, the belief in fairies lingered longer than elsewhere – about the year 1770. When he was a young man, the spirit of emulation was stirred in his breast by the example of the poet Burns. And so, as he wandered through the pastoral solitudes, keeping his sheep, he carried an ink-horn slung from his neck, and taught himself to write – and so committed his first poem to paper. And as he thus wandered and mused, he is said to have fallen asleep one day, upon a green hill-side, to dream the dream of Kilmeny, and to bear her image in his heart for ever after.

The story of Kilmeny is that of a girl of poetic nature, a lover of solitude, who, wandering alone at twilight, disappears in a wild glen among the hills. She is sought for by her friends – at first hopefully, at last despairingly. No trace of her is found. Years pass, and the mystery remains unsolved; but at the close of the seventh year, in the same twilight hour in which she had vanished, Kilmeny returns to her home. She has been rapt away by fairies, with whom the intervening years have been spent. But in the midst of

Fairyland, her heart still yearns tenderly to her home; and when seven years have expired, and the fairies have no longer power to detain her against her will, she chooses to leave the life of pleasure which she leads among them, to return to the common earth. Such is an outline of the story; but the story is the least part of the poem. Its charm lies in its exquisitely flowing and melodious verse, in its suggestion of the twilight world, and of a world of shadows – 'a land where all things are forgotten' – in its wistful tenderness; in a word, in the unique and perfect aptness of the style to the subject. So magical, indeed, are the fairy touches throughout the writings of the Ettrick Shepherd, that one might almost be tempted to dream that the experience with which tradition credits Thomas the Rhymer had been shared by this rhymer of a later day.

As in England, tales of fairies caught sight of on the country green, at twilight or by moonlight, of services rendered by mortals to fairies and gratefully and gracefully repaid, find a place among the fables of the Scottish peasantry. But it is by no means in such airy, gracious, and harmless if not beneficent, creations as this that the genius of the Scottish nation finds its fancy's most congenial food. That genius is upon the whole essentially a sombre one – relieved, indeed, by a rough humour – but tending most to an affinity with gloom. The hostility of Nature, its permanence as contrasted with the transient character of man, its victoriousness in the never-ending battle waged against it by man – a battle in which he fights for life, in which he gains a few trifling and temporary advantages, but in which he must recognise from the first that he fights against impossible odds: these are facts which a barren soil and a bleak and stormy climate have thrust forcibly upon the Scottish popular imagination, and which have impressed themselves deeply upon it. The shepherd battling for his life, and for the lives of his flock, against the force and darkness of driving snow, is a far more characteristic Scottish figure than that of James Hogg asleep on the hillside, dreaming of Fairyland.

This gloomy view of Nature has tinged the superstitious beliefs, and through them the stories of the Scottish peasantry. And upon the back of this gloomy view of Nature has come a sense, stronger perhaps than is felt by any other nation, of fate and doom, of the mystery of life and death, of the cruelty of the inevitable, the pain of separation, the darkness which enshrouds the whole. In this sense the Scotch are a nation of pessimists. They have found their religious vocation in Calvinism, the gloomiest and most terrible of creeds; and the spirit which embraced Calvinism like a bride informs their mythology and their fireside tales. Their tendency to devil-worship – to the propitiation of evil spirits – is illustrated by the hideous usage of the Good-man's Croft – a plot of ground near a village which was left untilled, set apart for, and dedicated to, the Powers of Evil, in the hope that their malignity might be appeased by the sacrifice, and so that they might be induced to spare the crops on the surrounding fields. Of the state of superstitious dread in which some Scotchmen passed their lives, Mrs Grant, of Laggan, gives a further curious illustration when she tells us that, in the Highlands of her day, to boast, or to congratulate a friend, was to rashly court retribution; whilst to praise a babe upon the nurse's arm was to incur suspicion of wishing to bring down ill upon its head.

Holding such beliefs as these, it is not to be wondered at if, in their stories, the Scotch are the passed-masters of the weird. Their very nursery tales – many of them – would appear to have been conceived with a view to educating, for some strange purpose or other, the passions of horror and sorrow in the child to whom they are told. Such rhymes, for instance, as 'The Tempted Lady', 'The Fause Knight and the Wee Boy', 'The Strange Visitor', are uncanny to a degree. In the two former, the Evil One himself appears, in specious guise. The Strange Visitor is Death. The nursery ballad of 'The Croodin' Doo' – a term of affection applied to a child – is as full of combined piteousness and sinister suggestion of underhand wickedness as any little tragedy of its length could well be. The suggestion is that of a man's childless, lawful wife bearing a bitter grudge against another woman who has borne him a child. The babe returns from a day's outing, and is questioned by his slighted mother as to where he has been, and what he has done. But he is tired, and cries out to be put to bed. The jealous woman, however, persists in her interrogatory, and asks him what he has had for dinner. He replies that he has dined off 'a little four-footed fish'. (The eft, or newt, is, like the toad, in the common superstition, venomous.) 'And what was done with the bones of this singular fish?' asks the woman. They were given to the lap-dog. And what did the dog do? After eating them, he 'shot out his feet and died'. There, with admirable art, the ballad ends. Its effect is immensely heightened by a burden, or refrain, in which, at the close of every verse, the child, with wearisome iteration, and with child-like importunity, cries out to his mother to 'make his bed soon'. This little song of child-life is queer fare to set before a child.

Stoddart, the tourist, long ago pointed out the contrast between the fairies of the English popular mythology and those of the Scotch;[1] and certainly the delicate, joyous,

[1]*Remarks on Local Scenery and Manners in Scotland*, vol. ii., p. 66 (1801).

tricksy, race of moonlight revellers whom we meet in the pages of Shakespeare are scarcely to be recognised as belonging to the same family with the soulless, man-stealing, creations of the Scottish peasant's fancy. The effect exercised upon popular superstition by the ruling passion of Calvinistic religion is one of the most striking things in Scottish folklore. For example, the belief in fairies did not cease to exist. It does not seem even to have been universally discountenanced by the Church; for we find mention of cases in which Ministers of the Gospel combine with their parishioners to take measures for the restitution of infants which the fairies had changed at nurse, or for the recovery of women who had been spirited away. And, indeed, two of the most curious pieces of composition known to me are, a pamphlet on the Second Sight, written by a Minister of Tiree, and an article on the Fairies, written by a Minister of Aberfoyle – both in the Seventeenth Century. Both writers were obviously firm believers in the superstitions upon which they wrote; and in both cases the gross ignorance and darkness of the writer's mind is only equalled by the authoritative weight and pedantry of his style. The Solemn League and Covenant had left its mark even upon the fairies, as the touching little story of 'The Fairy and the Bible-reader' shows.

The fairies, and that rough, grotesque, humoursome, but good-natured figure, the Brownie, occupy, however, but a small space in the popular mythology in comparison with such shapes of awe, of terror, or of ill-omen, as the ghosts, 'more real than living man', which the Highland Ezekiel saw borne past him on the wind, in Morven of the gloomy skies; or as the witch, the wraith, the 'warning', the water-kelpy, the man or woman who has the 'second sight', the evil or lost spirit.

The characteristic rough humour of the Scottish peasant, as it affects the creations of the fancy, embodies itself almost exclusively in the Brownie. This was a half-human creature, of uncouth appearance.

> 'His matted head on his breast did rest;
> A lang blue beard wan'er'd down like a vest; –
> But the glare o' his e'e hath nae bard exprest.'

During the day he would lurk in out-of-the-way corners of some old house which he had chosen to inhabit; and in the night-time would make himself useful to the family to which he had attached himself. But the conditions of his service were the most disinterested ever drawn up, and on the slightest attempt being made to reward him for his labours he would disappear for ever. The Brown Man of the Moors is another of these twilight, or half-seen, creations; but he is not of a domestic character. Wanderers upon lonely moors might, on rare occasions, catch a glimpse of him squatting in a hollow – a short, thick, powerful figure; earth-coloured, or of the tint of the surrounding ling. 'Shellycoat' dwelt in the waters. He was accustomed to appear decked out with the spoils of the sea – his coat being hung with shells, which clattered as he moved; and his delight was in mischief – such as, for instance, like the Spunkie, or Will-o'-the-Wisp, in leading travellers astray. 'Nuckelavee', the Sea-Devil of the Orkney Islanders, a more formidable figure, seemed to be shaped like a man above and like a horse below; and his peculiar horror lay in the fact that, being skinless, his raw, red flesh was exposed to view. Then there was the River Horse, a supernatural being supposed to feed, in the shape of a horse, on the shores of Loch Lochy, and when disturbed to plunge into its waters. The River Bull emerged from the lake to visit the cow-pastures; and there were cowherds who pretended that they could distinguish the calves of which he was the sire. Most of these creatures of the fancy are peculiar to the Scotch; and one cannot help fondly speculating as to the poetic use which Shakespeare would have made of them, had they happened to be among the associations of his childhood. But a more subtle water-spirit than any of those yet mentioned was the Kelpy, whose appearances were generally timed either to give warning of death by drowning, or to lure men to a watery grave. The Kelpy story of *The Doomed Rider*, to be found in the present collection, admirably illustrates the sentiment of fatalism inherent in the Scottish peasant's mind. In illustration of the kindred feeling of the 'malevolence of Nature', inherent there also, the poet Alexander Smith has aptly quoted the following popular rhyme – a dialogue in which two rivers are supposed to be the speakers:

'Said Tweed to Till,
What gars ye rin sae still?
Said Till to Tweed,
Though ye rin wi' speed,
And I rin slaw,
For every ane that ye droon
I droon twa!'

Here it appears that the elements are our enemies, and war against us to the death.

But, beyond a doubt, the most valuable element in the peasant tales, considered from the poetic standpoint, is not the fanciful or the imaginative element, but the human. This is, in some cases, brought out in extraordinary strength by the juxtaposition of the supernatural. Space allows me to cite but a single instance. By far the strangest, the most startling, and to us the most incomprehensible, of all the Scottish superstitions is the belief in the periodical return of the dead to their former homes – not as night-walking ghosts, encountered only by solitary persons in the dark – but as social beings, come back to join the family circle, and share in its festivities; in short, in the old phrase, come back 'to dine and dance with the living'. How anything so incredible should ever have come to be believed, we may well be at a loss to understand. Yet believed it seems to have been. There are two of the old ballads which are concerned with the belief, and they are two of the most beautiful which have come down to us.

The fragment entitled *The Wife of Usher's Well* sets forth how a thriving country-woman made provision for her three sons by sending them to sea. But they have not been long away from her, when she hears that they have perished in a storm. Then, in the madness of her grief, she puts up a blasphemous prayer to heaven, praying that the conflict of wind and wave may never cease until her sons come home to her, in their likeness as she knew them of old. Her prayer is heard, and answered.

> 'It fell about the Martinmas,
>   When nights are lang and mirk,
> The carline wife's three sons cam' hame,
>   And their hats were o' the birk.[1]

---

[1] That is, the birch. A 'syke' is a marshy bottom, with a small stream in it. A 'sheuch' is a sort of swamp. The small natural birch-tree, common in a hill-country, is often found on such ground.

'It neither grew in syke nor glen,
　　Nor yet in ony sheuch;
But, at the gates of Paradise,
　　That birk grew fair eneuch!'

Rising to a height of simple, unconscious, tragic irony, which is little less than sublime, the ballad goes on to detail the domestic preparations made by the mother to *fête* the homecoming of her sons. In a fever of happiness over the restoration of her lost ones, she issues her orders to her maids. The fatted calf is slain, and so on; and a brief hour of joy goes by. Then, as it grows late, the young men betake themselves to rest. The mother has prepared their bed with her own hands. But the dawn draws near – the period of their sojourn is almost up. The cock crows; and they recognise the signal for their departure.

'Up then crew the red, red, cock,
　　And up and crew the grey:
The eldest to the youngest said,
　　"'Tis time we were away!"

'The cock he hadna craw'd but ance,
　　Nor clapt his wings at a',
When the youngest to the eldest said,
　　"Brother, we must awa.

'"The cock doth craw, the day doth daw,
　　The channerin' worm doth chide;
Gin we be miss'd out o' our place,
　　A sair pain we maun bide.

'"Then, fare-ye-weel, my mither dear
    Fareweel to barn and byre!
And fare-ye-weel, the bonny lass
    That kin'les my mither's fire!"'

In this instance, the superstition of the return of the dead to their homes, to visit their friends, is complicated with the idea of punishment for a rash utterance, or impious prayer. But in the other ballad which deals with the same theme – *The Clerk's Twa Sons o' Owsenford* – the fundamental idea appears in its simplest form. In other respects the two stories resemble each other; except that, in the second case, the young men, two in number, are represented as paying the penalty of death – like the cavaliers of the *Tour de Nesle* – 'for a little of dear-boucht love', and that their home-coming is timed at Christmas.

These two tales are probably the wildest in the whole range of Scottish popular story; but, wild as they are, they contain, I think, a distinct and deep human significance. It will be observed that, in either case, the homecoming of the dead is placed at a season of relaxation and festivity – at Martinmas, namely, in the one case, and at Christmas in the other. At such seasons as these, the thoughts of the working-people, set free for a space from their daily occupations, are at liberty to wander; whilst it is a fact that the annual recurrence of such red-letter days, or land-marks in time, with their familiar accompaniment of ceremonies and usages, brings bygone years before the mind with a peculiar clearness – or, at least, brings them before the minds of people who lead simple, monotonous, lives, with few events to vary them. Nothing is commoner at such seasons than to hear people refer to the friends whom they have lost since that time last year, dwelling, as they do so, upon the characters, ways, and particular acts of the departed. Well, from this peculiar vividness of mental realisation, it is, for a bold and poetic imagination, but a single step to conjure up the actual bodily presence of the lost ones. Hence may have arisen these wild stories; and hence, no doubt, arose the fancy – a beautiful and touching one, I think, – that at Christmas the dead return to their homes to dine and dance with the living.

The few specimens at which we have now glanced must suffice to illustrate for us the more striking characteristics of the Scottish peasant-tales generally; these characteristics being, as I take it: first, an ever lively and inventive fancy. Secondly, a powerful imagination. The Scottish peasant story-teller is, like Homer, εὐφαντασίωτφς – '*qui sibi res, voces, actus, secundum verum, optime fingit*', as Quintilian hath it – we should say, perhaps, that he had 'poetic vision'; but the phrase does not cover quite the same ground. And this powerful imagination is apt to be gloomily affected, and at times distempered, by the natural features of the country, the conditions of life there, and the broodings of the national mind. Thirdly, a love of humanity, coupled with a keen sense of the hardness of its lot, manifesting itself in a poignant pathos. Of course, in a country of mixed races, like Scotland, the general characteristics of the tales vary widely in different parts of the country. The Celt of the West Highlands, for instance, has a *penchant* for giants, and a perfect callousness of the feelings – at which it is impossible not to marvel – where the lives and sufferings of the said giants and of their belongings are concerned. In one word, the giant of the West Highland tales is always 'fair game' – you cannot, by any contrivance, take a mean advantage of him. Again, the trolls, trows, 'hill-folk', or 'grey neighbours', of the Norsemen of the Shetland Islands have a character of their own, distinct from that of the fairies of the rest of Scotland, and harmonising perfectly with the colourless landscape of their native melancholy shores. In general terms, it may perhaps be said that the Highland tales display the more inexhaustibly luxuriant invention, whilst those of the Lowlands have the advantage of a more clearly defined outline, and enjoy a monopoly in depth of human significance.

To glance now at the literary bearing of these tales. In this respect, the oral traditions of the Scottish peasantry have enjoyed particular advantages, from the fact that the rich mine which they afford has been industriously and admirably worked by modern Scottish writers. Perhaps the most marked features of Scottish poetry have been, in the earlier times, its national, and in later times its popular, character. Well, in modern times at least, both of these characteristics have been shared by Scottish prose. This may not indeed be true, or at least not without large reservations, of the writings of Smollett; but, from Smollett's day onward, the Scottish prose *belles-lettres* have been essentially a 'growth of the soil'. And the Scotchmen who have laboured the field of popular tradition have been far from working it upon the lines of such writers as, for instance, Musæus, Tieck, and La Motte Fouqué – making the popular tale a mere foundation upon which to rear their own structures of philosophy or fancy, and often transforming it almost, if not quite, beyond recognition. Neither have they worked in the spirit of such a writer as Théophile Gautier, who, though he would sometimes use the popular tale as material to work on, had, in this regard, nothing national about him, being before all things a 'stylist' – an artist, pure and simple, indifferent, isolated from ties of country, from ties of kindred, almost from ties of humanity.

The Scottish writers, on the other hand, are, in the first case, *objective;* and, in the second, highly *national.*

First and foremost among these writers ranks, of course, Sir Walter Scott. Neglected as, in comparison with his other books, his *Border Minstrelsy* has been, the fact remains that he produced no more highly characteristic work; whilst of that great literature of fiction of which he afterwards became the author, the best and most vital parts may, I think, truly be said to 'have their roots in the hearts of the people'. And the further he departs from that source of his inspiration, the less valuable his work becomes. Though not born in the peasant class himself, Sir Walter knew the Scottish peasantry, in his own way, as few men have known them, and he lived on terms of friendly intimacy with his valued Tom Purdies and Swanstons, and of close literary confidence with such men as William Laidlaw and Joseph Train.

The two writers who rank next in the group alluded to were however, peasants born. James Hogg has already been spoken of. Allan Cunningham, born in 1784, was a son of the land-steward on the estate on which Robert Burns occupied a farm – a circumstance which, no doubt, had its effect in stimulating the poetic impulse that was in him. On growing up, he adopted the trade of a mason. An antiquarian, Cromek by name, was at that time engaged in forming a collection of 'Remains of Galloway and Nithsdale Song', on the model of Percy's *Reliques*; and he applied to young Cunningham to collect old poems for him. 'Honest Allan', as his friend Thomas Carlyle styled him, was not successful in his quest; but, nothing daunted, he set to work to compose songs and ballads which, if they could not in the nature of things possess the quality of age, should at least be as good as old, or better if possible. These he transmitted to his employer; without explanation. Cromek's love for antiquity would appear to have been a pure passion, inasmuch as he seems to have loved it for the sake of any κῦδος, or profit, which was to be derived from the attachment, and for no other reason. He was delighted with his young correspondent's contributions to the 'Remains of Galloway and Nithsdale Song'; and Cunningham's literary career was thus begun. His *Traditional Tales of the English and Scottish Peasantry* are perhaps the best of the many books which he wrote; and are especially distinguished by the sweetness of his style, and by the picturesque traits of old-fashioned country-life and the exquisite touches of fresh nature-painting in which they abound.

After Cunningham comes Campbell of Isla, born in 1822. He was of gentle birth, but understood and sympathised with the peasantry. A proficient in the Gaelic language, he went about on foot among the people of the West Highlands and Islands – like a sort of Romany Rye, or like Catskin, the Wandering Young Gentleman of the *Garland* – and got them to tell him stories, which he accurately noted down. In his writings, therefore, we get the stories as nearly as possible in the exact words in which they were told. He died about six or seven years ago.

Then there is Dougal Graham, the chap-book writer, who has been called the 'Scottish Rabelais'. He began life as a chapman, and came in course of time to be *skellat* bell-man of Glasgow. His *magnum opus* is a metrical narrative of the Jacobite Rising of '45, in which he himself took part; and to him are also attributed the invention of Turnimspike, and John Cheap, and the history of the Witty Exploits of George Buchanan, the King's Jester.

Then, after Graham, come Robert Chambers – whose

fame as a publisher has somewhat obscured his well-earned fame as a writer; Hugh Miller, the geologist; and, among men of merely local reputation, James Telfer, of Saughtree, and many others.

Literature takes the life of tradition, and then embalms the dead body. What stories, then, have taken the place, as genuine peasant-tales, though belonging to a period of decadence, of the old stories which introduce the supernatural and have ceased to be believed? Well, there are a variety, which do not tax the power of credulity quite too far. Stories of old local battles, for instance, and of how some neighbouring stream, or river, ran discoloured with blood for three whole days after the fighting. Stories of buried treasures: there is the English knight whom Jock of Heavyside slew, and who lies buried, in his silver armour, not far from Agricola's Camp at Pennymuir. Then there is a neighbouring treasure which lies, wrapt in a bullock's hide, buried in a hill. It is said, circumstantially enough, to have been concealed by two brothers, in time of war; but is described, with judicious vagueness, as lying exactly midway between two places, only one of which is known. A third treasure is more particularly localised. The field in which it lies buried is well known; but if any man set spade in that field to dig for it, the sky, we are told, will ere long grow dark, and a muttering of thunder will be heard, and a flash of lightning seen. (This story certainly does trench perilously near to superstition.) Then, again, there are other treasures, with which – even if one did happen to light upon one of them – it would not be safe to meddle. They are supposed to have been buried in a time of the plague – perhaps as sacrifices to appease some Unknown Power – and the infection of the pestilence is supposed to have been buried with them; so that, were they to be unearthed, the plague would probably break out again. On the sea-coast, sunken treasure-ships take the place of buried treasures. Then there are the stories of mysterious caverns, into which people enter, but from which they do not come out. There is one cave of this kind into which a huntsman and a pack of hounds are said to have pursued a hunted fox; but from which neither fox, hounds, huntsman, nor horse, were ever known to emerge again. Then there is another cave into which a piper penetrated, playing upon his pipes. He never came out either. His music was listened to for a long time by persons at the mouth of the cavern. At first it was loud and cheerful, then it grew fainter and fainter, more plaintive and more plaintive, until at last it died away in the bowels of the earth. Then, there are kindred stories of subterranean passages of great length – sometimes said to have been fashioned by the monks – uniting ancient castles or religious establishments. Then, there are modern varieties of the hero-tale – stories of fights, and of adventures by flood and field – a favourite one is that of a prodigious leap taken by the hero in escaping from pursuit. There are, also, stories of remarkable local characters – the desperate ones being preferred. There is, for instance, the sceptical country-gentleman, who, having led a merry life and scoffed at the Minister, preserved at least the virtue of consistency by leaving directions in his will that he was to be buried, in a vaulted chamber, seated at a table, with a church-warden pipe in his mouth, and a bottle and a glass before him. Or else there is that other reprobate, who, when lands were gone and money spent, resolved to put an end to his life. So he blindfolded a favourite mare, mounted her, and rode towards the cliff-heads. There he put her to the gallop, and prepared for a leap into space. But, just as she reached the brink, by some instinct the blind mare swerved and turned. He set her at the frightful leap again, and again she refused; and, after a third failure, he is said to have seen the error of his ways, and to have ridden home, and from that day to have led a reformed life. Then, lastly, there is the murder-tale – the narrative of some desperate deed. It must not be hastily classed with the literature of the 'penny dreadful' and the 'shilling shocker' order; for, whatever may be the shortcomings of Arcady, vulgarity at least is not one of them – and the peasant-tales never sink to so low a level as that. Blood may be spilt in them – and spilt freely it often is; but there are always present redeeming touches of fancy, of poetry, of character-painting, of the picturesque, to raise the terrible histories from the rank of the 'sensation novel' to that of the poetic tragedy.

What, in conclusion, is there in these rude 'old-wives' tales' to justify their withdrawal from the limbo of forgotten things? They have a place, though it be a humble one, in the history of the workings of the human mind. They are the manifestation, in its simplest form, of the literary, or poetic, impulse; and nothing that has been thus generated, and that has stood the test of time as these tales have done, can ever, I believe, be unworthy of our study. To take an instance from another art. Anthropologists tell us that, ages and ages ago, there was a savage, dwelling in a cave, in a bleak northern country, among mountains which were covered with pine-trees. He was agile, able-bodied, and ingenious; and he faced the mighty beasts of the forest in his hunting, to obtain food for his wife and children. We know next to nothing about him; but we do know that, one day, it somehow occurred to him to make a drawing on the wall of his cave of something which he had seen and had no doubt admired. So he etched a little picture of a reindeer, copying faithfully, the outline of the body, and the branchings of the antlers. This, reader, is the man whom we speak of as Paleolithic Man. His performance had the innate permanence, from a human point of view, of all true art. It remains, and it continues to interest, to this day; for it is the outcome of the first faint stirrings in the human breast of two passions: the Love of Beauty, and the Thirst for Fame. 'One touch of nature makes the whole world kin.' The lapse of countless centuries does not prevent our entering into the feelings of that simple artist; and what he felt, in his day and hour, is felt, in their degree, by the tellers of the Tales of the Scottish Peasantry. Art is not only a thing of bound volumes and of exhibitions; and the Scottish peasant has shown perhaps as keen a sense of it – of the story-teller's art, at least – as his mental development and the conditions of his existence would admit.[1]

GEORGE DOUGLAS

[1]The substance of this Introduction was delivered as a Lecture at the Royal Institution, January 29th, 1892.

NOTE

The Editor desires to return his best thanks to the following authors, publishers, and proprietors: To Mr W. Traill Dennison, of West Brough, Sanday, Orkney Islands, for his admirable original version of the story of 'Assipattle and the Mester Stoorworm', as well as for leave to reprint from the *Scottish Antiquary* the story of 'Nuckelavee'; to Mr John Kennedy, of Trinafour, for four stories collected in the Athole district of Perthshire; and to Mr J. G. Ollason, of Lerwick, for two unpublished Shetland fairy-tales; also to Mr W. W. Gibbings, for permission to reprint three stories from his *Folklore and Legends: Scotland*; and to the Council of the Folk-Lore Society, for leave to print extracts from their publications.

Scottish Folk and Fairy Tales

Nursery Stories

THE STORY OF THE WHITE PET*

There was a farmer before now who had a White Pet,[1] and when Christmas was drawing near, he thought that he would kill the White Pet. The White Pet heard that, and he thought he would run away; and that is what he did.

He had not gone far when a bull met him. Said the bull to him, 'All hail! White Pet, where art thou going?' 'I,' said the White Pet, 'am going to seek my fortune; they were going to kill me for Christmas, and I thought I had better run away.' 'It is better for me,' said the bull, 'to go with thee, for they were going to do the very same with me.'

'I am willing,' said the White Pet; 'the larger the party the better the fun.'

They went forward till they fell in with a dog.

'All hail! White Pet,' said the dog. 'All hail! thou dog.' 'Where art thou going?' said the dog.

*J. F. Campbell, *Popular Tales of the West Highlands*.
[1]A lamb brought up by hand.

'I am running away, for I heard that they were threatening to kill me for Christmas.'

'They were going to do the very same to me,' said the dog, 'and I will go with you.' 'Come, then,' said the White Pet.

They went then, till a cat joined them. 'All hail! White Pet,' said the cat. 'All hail! oh cat.'

'Where art thou going?' said the cat. 'I am going to seek my fortune,' said the White Pet, 'because they were going to kill me at Christmas.'

'They were talking about killing me too,' said the cat, 'and I had better go with you.'

'Come on then,' said the White Pet.

Then they went forward till a cock met them. 'All hail! White Pet,' said the cock. 'All hail to thyself! oh cock,' said the White Pet. 'Where,' said the cock, 'art thou going?' 'I,' said the White Pet, 'am going away, for they were threatening my death at Christmas.'

'They were going to kill me at the very same time,' said the cock, 'and I will go with you.'

'Come, then,' said the White Pet.

They went forward till they fell in with a goose. 'All hail! White Pet,' said the goose. 'All hail to thyself! oh goose,' said the White Pet. 'Where art thou going?' said the goose.

'I,' said the White Pet, 'am running away, because they were going to kill me at Christmas.'

'They were going to do that to me too,' said the goose, 'and I will go with you.'

The party went forward till the night was drawing on them, and they saw a little light far away; and though far off, they were not long getting there. When they reached the house, they said to each other that they would look in at the window to see who was in the house, and they saw thieves counting money; and the White Pet said, 'Let every one of us call his own call. I will call my own call; and let the bull call his own call; let the dog call his own call; and the cat her own call; and the cock his own call; and the goose his own call.' With that they gave out one shout – GAIRE!

When the thieves heard the shouting that was without, they thought the mischief was there; and they fled out, and they went to a wood that was near them. When the White Pet and his company saw that the house was empty, they went in and they got the money that the thieves had been counting, and they divided it amongst themselves; and then they thought that they would settle to rest. Said the White Pet, 'Where wilt thou sleep tonight, oh bull?' 'I will sleep,' said the bull, 'behind the door where I used' (to be). 'Where wilt thou sleep thysell, White Pet?' 'I will sleep,' said the White Pet, 'in the middle of the floor where I used' (to be). 'Where wilt thou sleep, oh dog?' said the White Pet. 'I will sleep beside the fire where I used' (to be), said the dog. 'Where wilt thou sleep, oh cat?' 'I will sleep,' said the cat, 'in the candle press, where I like to be.' 'Where wilt thou sleep, oh cock?' said the White Pet. 'I,' said the cock, 'will sleep on the rafters where I used' (to be). 'Where wilt thou sleep, oh goose?' 'I will sleep,' said the goose, 'on the midden,[1] where I was accustomed to be.'

They were not long settled to rest, when one of the thieves returned to look in to see if he could perceive if any one at all was in the house. All things were still, and he went on forward to the candle press for a candle, that he might kindle to make him a light; but when he put his hand in the box the cat thrust her claws into his hand, but he

[1]Dung-heap.

took a candle with him, and he tried to light it. Then the dog got up, and he stuck his tail into a pot of water that was beside the fire; he shook his tail and put out the candle. Then the thief thought that the mischief was in the house, and he fled; but when he was passing the White Pet, he gave him a blow; before he got past the bull, he gave him a kick; and the cock began to crow; and when he went out, the goose began to belabour him with his wings about the shanks.

He went to the wood where his comrades were, as fast as was in his legs. They asked him how it had gone with him. 'It went,' said he, 'but middling; when I went to the candle press, there was a man in it who thrust ten knives into my hand; and when I went to the fireside to light the candle, there was a big black man lying there, who was sprinkling water on it to put it out; and when I tried to go out, there was a big man in the middle of the floor, who gave me a shove; and another man behind the door who pushed me out; and there was a little brat on the loft calling out CUIR-ANEES-AN-SHAW-AY-S-FONI-MI-HAYN-DA – Send him up here and I'll do for him; and there was a shoemaker out on the midden, belabouring me about the shanks with his apron.'

When the thieves heard that, they did not return to seek their lot of money; and the White Pet and his comrades got it to themselves; and it kept them peaceably as long as they lived.

THE MILK-WHITE DOO[*][1]

There was once a man that wrought in the fields, and had a wife, and a son, and a dochter. One day he caught a hare, and took it hame to his wife, and bade her make it ready for his dinner. While it was on the fire, the goodwife aye tasted and tasted at it, till she had tasted it a' away, and then she didna ken what to do for her goodman's dinner. So she cried in Johnie her son to come and get his head kaimed ; and when she was kaiming his head, she slew him, and put him into the pat. Well, the goodman cam hame to his dinner, and his wife set down Johnie well boiled to him; and when he was eating, he takes up a foot, and says: 'That's surely my Johnie's fit.'

'Sic nonsense! it's ane o' the hare's,' says the goodwife.

Syne he took up a hand, and says: 'That's surely my Johnie's hand.'

'Ye're havering,[2] goodman; it's anither o' the hare's feet.'

So when the goodman had eaten his dinner, little Katy, Johnie's sister, gathered a' the banes, and put them in below a stane at the cheek o' the door –

> Where they grew, and they grew,
> To a milk-white doo,
> That took its wings,
> And away it flew.

And it flew till it cam to where twa women were washing claes, and it sat down on a stane, and cried –

*Robert Chambers, *Popular Rhymes of Scotland*.
[1]Pigeon.
[2]Talking nonsense.

'Pew, pew,
My minny me slew,
My daddy me chew,
My sister gathered my banes,
And put them between twa milk-white stanes;
And I grew, and I grew,
To a milk-white doo,
And I took to my wings, and away I flew.'

'Say that owre again, my bonny bird, and we'll gie ye a' thir claes,' says the women.

'Pew, pew,
My minny me slew,' etc.

And it got the claes; and then flew till it cam to a man counting a great heap o' siller, and it sat down and cried –

'Pew, pew,
My minny me slew,' etc.

'Say that again, my bonny bird, and I'll gie ye a' this siller,' says the man.

'Pew, pew,
My minny me slew,' etc.

And it got a' the siller; and syne it flew till it cam to twa millers grinding corn, and it cried –

'Pew, pew,
My minny me slew,' etc.

'Say that again, my bonny bird, and I'll gie ye this mill-stane,' says the miller.

> 'Pew, pew,
> My minny me slew,' etc.

And it gat the millstane; and syne it flew till it lighted on its father's house-top. It threw sma' stanes down the lum,[1] and Katy cam out to see what was the matter; and the doo threw all the claes to her. Syne the father cam out, and the doo threw a' the siller to him. And syne the mother cam out, and the doo threw down the millstane upon her and killed her. And at last it flew away; and the goodman and his dochter after that

> Lived happy, and died happy,
> And never drank out of a dry cappy.

THE CROODIN DOO[2]*

> 'Where hae ye been a' the day,
> My bonny wee croodin doo?'
> 'O I hae been at my stepmother's house;
> Make my bed, mammie, now!
> Make my bed, mammie, now!'

> 'Where did ye get your dinner,
> My bonny wee croodin doo?'
> 'I got it in my stepmother's;
> Make my bed, mammie, now, now, now!
> Make my bed, mammie, now!'

[1]Chimney.
[2]A term of endearment applied to a child; literally, 'cooing dove'.
*Chambers, *Popular Rhymes of Scotland*.

'What did she gie ye to your dinner,
My bonny wee croodin doo?'
'She ga'e me a little four-footed fish;
Make my bed, mammie, now, now, now!
Make my bed, mammie, now !'

'Where got she the four-footed fish,
My bonny wee croodin doo?'
'She got it down in yon well strand;
O make my bed, mammie, now, now, now!
Make my bed, mammie, now!'

'What did she do wi' the banes o't,
My bonny wee croodin doo?'
'She ga'e them to the little dog;
Make my bed, mammie, now, now, now!
Make my bed, mammie, now!'

'O what became o' the little dog,
My bonny wee croodin doo?'
'O it shot out its feet and died!
O make my bed, mammie, now, now, now I
O make my bed, niammic, now!'

THE CATTIE SITS IN THE KILN-RING SPINNING*

The cattie sits in the kiln-ring,
            Spinning, spinning;
And by came a little wee mousie,
            Rinning, rinning.

*Chambers, *Popular Rhymes of Scotland*.

'O what's that you're spinning, my loesome,
        Loesome lady?'
'I'm spinning a sark[1] to my young son,'
        Said she, said she.

'Weel mot he brook it, my loesome,
        Loesome lady.'
'Gif he dinna brook it weel, he may brook it ill,'
        Said she, said she.

'I soopit[2] my house, my loesome,
        Loesome lady.'
''Twas a sign ye didna sit amang dirt then,'
        Said she, said she.

'I fand twall pennies, my winsome,
        Winsome lady.'
''Twas a sign ye warna sillerless,'[3]
        Said she, said she.

'I gaed to the market, my loesome,
        Loesome lady.'
''Twas a sign ye didna sit at hame then,'
        Said she, said she.

'I coft[4] a sheepie's head, my winsome,
        Winsome lady.'
''Twas a sign ye warna kitchenless,'
        Said she, said she.

'I put it in my pottie to boil, my loesome,
        Loesome lady.'
''Twas a sign ye didna eat it raw,'
        Said she, said she.

[1]Shirt.   [3]Without money.
[2]Swept.   [4]Bought.

'I put it in my winnock[1] to cool, my winsome,
       Winsome lady.'
''Twas a sign ye didna burn your chafts[2] then,'
       Said she, said she.

'By came a cattie, and ate it a' up, my loesome,
       Loesome lady.'
'And sae will I you – worrie, worrie – gnash, gnash,'
       Said she, said she.

MARRIAGE OF ROBIN REDBREAST
AND THE WREN*

There was an auld grey Poussie Baudrons,[3] and she gaed awa' down by a water-side, and there she saw a wee Robin Redbreast happin' on a brier; and Poussie Baudrons says: 'Where's tu gaun, wee Robin?' And wee Robin says: 'I'm gaun awa' to the king to sing him a sang this guid Yule morning.' And Poussie Baudrons says: 'Come here, wee Robin, and I'll let you see a bonny white ring round my neck.' But wee Robin says: 'Na, na! grey Poussie Baudrons; na, na! Ye worry't the wee mousie; but ye'se no worry me.' So wee Robin flew awa' till he came to a fail fauld-dike,[4] and there he saw a grey greedy gled[5] sitting. And grey greedy gled says: 'Where's tu gaun, wee Robin?' And wee Robin says: 'I'm gaun awa' to the king to sing him a sang this guid Yule morning.' And grey greedy gled says: 'Come here, wee Robin, and I'll let you see a bonny feather in my wing.' But wee Robin says: 'Na, na! grey

*Chambers, *Popular Rhymes of Scotland*.   [3]Pussy cat.
[1]Window.   [4]Turf wall enclosing a field.   [5]Kite
[2]Chaps, mouth.

greedy gled; na,na! Ye pookit[1] a' the wee lintie;[2] but ye'se
no pook me.' So wee Robin flew awa' till he caine to the
cleuch o' a craig,[3] and there he saw slee Tod Lowrie[4]
sitting. And slee Tod Lowrie says: 'Where's tu gaun, wee
Robin?' And wee Robin says: 'I'm gaun awa' to the king to
sing him a sang this guid Yule morning.' And slee Tod
Lowrie says: 'Come here, wee Robin, and I'll let ye see a
bonny spot on the tap o' my tail.' But wee Robin says: 'Na,
na! slee Tod Lowrie; na, na! Ye worry't the wee lammie;
but ye'se no worry me.' So wee Robin flew awa' till he
came to a bonny burn-side, and there he saw a wee callant[5]
sitting. And the wee callant says: 'Where's tu gaun, wee
Robin?' And wee Robin says: 'I'm gaun awa' to the king to
sing him a sang this guid Yule morning.' And the wee
callant says: 'Come here, wee Robin, and I'll gie ye a wheen
grand moolins[6] out o' my pooch.' But wee Robin says: 'Na,
na! wee callant; na, na! Ye speldert the gowdspink; but
ye'se no spelder me.' So wee Robin flew awa' till he came
to the king, and there he sat on a winnock sole,[7] and sang
the king a bonny sang. And the king says to the queen:
'What'll we gie to wee Robin for singing us this bonny
sang?' And the queen says to the king: 'I think we'll gie him
the wee wran to be his wife.' So wee Robin and the wee
wran were married, and the king, and the queen, and a' the
court danced at the waddin'; syne he flew awa' hame to his
ain water-side, and happit on a brier.

[1]Pluck, strip.   [2]Linnet.   [3]Face of a rock.   [7]Window sill.
[4]Mister Fox.   [5]Boy.   [6]Some crumbs.

THE TEMPTED LADY*

'Noo, lasses, ye should never be owre proud; for ye see there was ance a leddy, and she was aye fond o' being brawer than other folk; so she gaed awa' to take a walk ae day, her and her brother: so she met wi' a gentleman – but it was nae gentleman in reality, but Auld Nick himsel', who can change himsel' brawly into a gentleman – a' but the cloven feet; but he keepit them out o' sight. So he began to make love to the young leddy:

> "I'll gie you a pennyworth o' preens,[1]
> That's aye the way that love begins;
> If ye'll walk with me, leddy, leddy,
> If ye'll walk with me, leddy."

> "I'll no hae your pennyworth o' preens,
> That's no the way that love begins;
> And I'll no walk with you, with you,
> And I'll no walk with you."

> "O Johnie, O Johnie, what can the matter be,
> That I love this leddy, and she loves na me?
> And for her sake I must die, must die,
> And for her sake I must die!"

> "I'll gie you a bonny silver box,
> With seven silver hinges, and seven silver locks,
> If ye'll walk," etc.

> "I'll no hae your bonny silver box,
> With seven silver hinges, and seven silver locks,
> And I'll no walk," etc.

> "O Johnie, O Johnie" [*as in third verse*].

*Chambers, *Popular Rhymes of Scotland*.   [1]Pins.

"But I'll gie you a bonnier silver box,
With seven golden hinges, and seven golden locks,
If ye'll walk," etc.

"I'll no hae" [*as in fifth verse*].

"O Johnie" [*as in third verse*].

"I'll gie you a pair O' bonny shoon,
The tane made in Sodom, the tother in Rome;
If ye'll walk," etc.

"I'll no hae" [*as in fifth verse*].

"O Johnie" [*as in third verse*].

"I'll gie you the half O' Bristol town,
With coaches rolling up and down,
If ye'll walk," etc.

"I'll no hae" [*as in fifth verse*].

"O Johnie" [*as in third verse*].

"I'll gie you the hale o', Bristol town,
With coaches rolling up and down,
If ye'll walk with me, leddy, leddy,
If ye'll walk with me, leddy."

"If ye'll gie me the hale o' Bristol town,
With coaches rolling up and down,
I will walk with you, with you,
And I will walk with you."

And aff he flew wi' her! Noo, lasses, ye see ye maun aye mind that.'

THE FAUSE KNIGHT AND THE WEE BOY*

'O where are ye gaun?'
  Quo' the fause knight upon the road;
'I'm gaun to the schule,'
  Quo' the wee boy, and still he stude.

'What is that upon your back?'
  Quo' the fause knight upon the road;
'Atweel it is my bukes,'
  Quo' the wee boy, and still he stude.

'What's that ye've got in your arm?'
  Quo' the fause knight upon the road;
'Atweel it is my peat,'[1]
  Quo' the wee boy, and still he stude.

'Wha's aucht thae sheep?'
  Quo' the fause knight upon the road;
'They're mine and my mother's,'
  Quo' the wee boy, and still he stude.

'How mony o' them are mine?'
  Quo' the fause knight upon the road;
'A' they that hae blue tails,'
  Quo' the wee boy, and still he stude.

'I wiss ye were on yon tree,'
  Quo' the fause knight upon the road;
'And a guid ladder under me,'
  Quo' the wee boy, and still he stude.

*Chambers, *Popular Rhymes of Scotland*.
[1] A contribution to the schoomaster's stock of fuel.

'And the ladder for to break,'
   Quo' the fause knight upon the road;
'And you for to fa' down,'
   Quo' the wee boy, and still he stude.

'I wiss ye were in yon sea,'
   Quo' the fause knight upon the road;
'And a guid bottom under me,'
   Quo' the wee boy, and still he stude.

'And the bottom for to break,'
   Quo' the fause knight upon the road;
'And ye to be drowned,'
   Quo' the wee boy, and still he stude.[1]

THE STRANGE VISITOR*

A wife was sitting at her reel ae night;
  And aye she sat, and aye she reeled, and aye she wished
    for company.

In came a pair o' braid braid soles, and sat down at the
    fireside;
  And aye she sat, etc.

In came a pair o' sma' sma' legs, and sat down on the
    braid braid soles;
  And aye she sat, etc.

---

[1]Motherwell gives the above, in his *Minstrelsy Ancient and Modern,* as a
nursery tale of Galloway, and a specimen of a class of compositions of
great antiquity, representing the Enemy of man in the endeavour to
confound some poor mortal with puzzling questions.
*Chambers, *Popular Rhymes of Scotland.*

In came a pair o' muckle muckle knees, and sat down on
     the sma' sma' legs;
And aye she sat, etc.

In came a pair o' sma' sma' thees, and sat down on the
     muckle muckle knees;
And aye she sat, etc.

In came a pair o' muckle muckle hips, and sat down on the
     sma' sma' thees;
And aye she sat, etc.

In' came a sma' sma' waist, and sat down on the muckle
     muckle hips;
And aye she sat, etc.

In came a pair o' braid braid shouthers, and sat down on
     the sma' sma' waist;
And aye she sat, etc.

In came a pair o' sma' sma' arms, and sat down on the
     braid braid shouth'ers;
And aye she sat, etc.

In came a pair o' muckle muckle hands, and sat down on
     the sma' sma' arms;
And aye she sat, etc.

In came a sma' sma' neck, and sat down on the braid braid
     shouthers;
And aye she sat, etc.

In came a great big head, and sat down on the sma' sma,' neck.

'What way hae ye sic braid braid feet?' quo' the wife.
'Muckle ganging, muckle ganging' (*gruffly*).
'What way hae ye sic sma' sma' legs?'
'*Aih-h-h!* – late – and *wee-e-e – moul*' (*whiningly*).
'What way hae ye sic muckle muckle knees?'
'Muckle praying, muckle praying' (*piously*).
'What way hae ye sic sma' sma' thees?'
'Aih-h-h! – late – and wee-e-e – moul' (*whiningly*).
'What way hae ye sic big big hips?'
'Muckle sitting, muckle sitting' (*gruffly*).
'What way hae ye sic a sma' sma' waist?'
'Aih-h-h! – late – and wee-e-e – moul' (*whiningly*).
'What way hae ye sic braid braid shouthers?'
'Wi' carrying broom, wi' carrying broom' (*gruffly*).
'What way hae ye sic sma' sma' arms?'
'Aih-h-h – late – and wee-e-e – moul' (*whiningly*).
'What way hae ye sic muckle muckle hands?'
'Threshing wi' an iron flail, threshing wi' an iron flail'
(*gruffly*).
'What way hae ye sic a sma' sma' neck?'
'Aih-h-h! – late – and wee-e-e – moul' (*pitifully*).
'What way hae ye sic a muckle muckle head?'
'Muckle wit, muckle wit' *(keenly)*.
'What do you come for?'
'FOR YOU!' (*At the top of the voice, with a wave* of *the arm and a stamp of the feet.*)[1]

RASHIN-COATIE*

Once, a long time ago, there was a gentleman had two lassies. The oldest was ugly and ill-natured, but the

[1]The figure is meant for that of Death.   *The Folk-Lore Journal.*

youngest was a bonnie lassie and good; but the ugly one was the favourite with her father and mother. So they ill-used the youngest in every way, and they sent her into the woods to herd cattle, and all the food she got was a little porridge and whey.

Well, amongst the cattle was a red calf, and one day it said to the lassie, 'Gee that porridge and whey to the doggie, and come wi' me.'

So the lassie followed the calf through the wood, and they came to a bonnie hoosie, where there was a nice dinner ready for them; and after they had feasted on everything nice they went back to the herding.

Every day the calf took the lassie away, and feasted her on dainties; and every day she grew bonnier. This disappointed the father and mother and the ugly sister. They expected that the rough usage she was getting would take away her beauty; and they watched and watched until they saw the calf take the lassie away to the feast. So they resolved to kill the calf; and not only that, but the lassie was to be compelled to kill him with an axe. Her ugly sister was to hold his head, and the lassie who loved him had to give the blow and kill him.

She could do nothing but greet;[1] but the calf told her not to greet, but to do as he bade her; and his plan was that instead of coming down on his head she was to come down on the lassie's head who was holding him, and then she was to jump on his back and they would run off. Well, the day came for the calf to be killed, and everything was ready – the ugly lassie holding his head, and the bonnie lassie armed with the axe. So she raised the axe, and came down on the ugly sister's head; and in the confusion that took place she got on the calf's back and they ran away. And

[1]Weep.

they ran and better nor ran till they came to a meadow where grew a great lot of rashes; and, as the lassie had not on many clothes, they pu'ed rashes, and made a coatie for her. And they set off again and travelled, and travelled, till they came to the king's house. They went in, and asked if they wanted a servant. The mistress said she wanted a kitchen lassie, and she would take Rashin-coatie. So Rashin-coatie said she would stop, if they keepit the calf too. They were willing to do that. So the lassie and the calf stoppit in the king's house, and everybody was well pleased with her; and when Yule came, they said she was to stop at home and make the dinner, while all the rest went to the kirk. After they were away the calf asked if she would like to go. She said she would, but she had no clothes, and she could not leave the dinner. The calf said he would give her clothes, and make the dinner too. He went out, and came back with a grand dress, all silk and satin, and such a nice pair of slippers. The lassie put on the dress, and before she left she said –

'Ilka peat gar anither burn,
An' ilka spit gar anither turn,
An' ilka pot gar anither play,
Till I come frae the kirk on gude Yule day.'

So she went to the kirk, and nobody kent it was Rashin-coatie. They wondered who the bonnie lady could be; and, as soon as the young prince saw her, he fell in love with her, and resolved he would find out who she was, before she got home; but Rashin-coatie left before the rest, so that she might get home in time to take off her dress, and look after the dinner.

When the prince saw her leaving, he made for the door to stop her; but she jumped past him, and in the hurry lost one of her shoes. The prince kept the shoe, and Rashin-coatie got home all right, and the folk said the dinner was very nice.

Now the prince was resolved to find out who the bonnie lady was, and he sent a servant through all the land with the shoe. Every lady was to try it on, and the prince promised to marry the one it would fit. That servant went to a great many houses, but could not find a lady that the shoe would go on, it was so little and neat. At last he came to a henwife's house, and her daughter had little feet. At first the shoe would not go on, but she paret her feet, and clippit her toes, until the shoes went on. Now the prince was very angry. He knew it was not the lady that he wanted; but, because he had promised to marry whoever the shoe fitted, he had to keep his promise.

The marriage day came, and, as they were all riding to the kirk, a little bird flew through the air, and it sang –

'Clippit feet an' paret taes is on the saidle set;
But bonnie feet an' braw feet sits in the kitchen neuk.'

'What's that ye say?' said, the prince. 'Oh,' says the hen-wife, 'would ye mind what a feel bird says?' But the prince said, 'Sing that again, bonnie birdie.' So the bird sings –

'Clippit feet an' paret taes is on the saidle set;
But bonnie feet an' braw feet sits in the kitchen neuk.'

The prince turned his horse and rode home, and went straight to his father's kitchen, and there sat Rashin-coatie. He kent her at once, she was so bonnie; and when she tried on the shoe it fitted her, and so the prince married Rashin-coatie, and they lived happy, and built a house for the red calf, who had been so kind to her.

STORIES OF ANIMALS

Stories of Animals*

THE FOX OUTWITTED

One day the fox succeeded in catching a fine fat goose asleep by the side of a loch; he held her by the wing, and making a joke of her cackling, hissing, and fears, he said –

'Now, if you had me in your mouth as I have you, tell me what you would do?'

'Why,' said the goose, 'that is an easy question. I would fold my hands, shut my eyes, say a grace, and then eat you.'

'Just what I mean to do,' said Rory;[1] and folding his hands, and looking very demure, he said a pious grace with his eyes shut.

But while he did this the goose had spread her wings, and she was now half way over the loch; so the fox was left to lick his lips for supper.

'I will make a rule of this,' he said in disgust, 'never in all my life to say a grace again till after I feel the meat warm in my belly.'

*J. F. Campbell, *Popular Tales of the West Highlands*.
[1]Rory is a corruption of a Gaelic proper name, which means, one whose hair is of the colour of the fox 'Ruadh'.

THE FOX TROUBLED WITH FLEAS

The fox is much troubled by fleas, and this is the way in which he gets rid of them. He hunts about till he finds a lock of wool, and then he takes it to the river, and holds it in his mouth, and so puts the end of his brush into the water, and down he goes slowly. The fleas run away from the water, and at last they all run over the fox's nose into the wool, and then the fox dips his nose under and lets the wool go off with the stream.[1]

THE FOX AND THE BAG-PIPES

The fox, being hungry one day, found a bag-pipe, and proceeded to eat the bag, which is generally, or was till lately, made of hide. There was still a remnant of breath in the bag, and when the fox bit it the drone gave a groan, when the fox, surprised but not frightened, said –

'Here is meat and music!'[2]

THE FOX'S STRATAGEM

The fox is very wise indeed. I don't know whether it is true or not, but an old fellow told me that he had seen him go to a loch where there were wild ducks, and take a bunch of heather in his mouth, then go into the water, and swim down with the wind till he got into the middle of the ducks, and then he let go the heather and killed two of them.

[1]This is told as a fact.
[2]A popular saying in the West Highlands.

THE FOX AND THE WRENS

A fox had noticed for some days a family of wrens, off which he wished to dine. He might have been satisfied with one, but he was determined to have the whole lot – father and eighteen sons – and all so like that he could not tell one from the other, or the father from the children.

'It is no use to kill one son,' he said to himself, 'because the old cock will take warning and fly away with the seventeen. I wish I knew which is the old gentleman.'

He set his wits to work to find out, and one day, seeing them all threshing in a barn, he sat down to watch them; still he could not be sure.

'Now I have it,' he said; 'well done the old man's stroke! He hits true,' he cried.

'Oh!' replied the one he suspected of being the head of the family; 'if you had seen my grandfather's strokes you might have said that.'

The sly fox pounced on the cock, ate him up in a trice, and then soon caught and disposed of the eighteen sons, all flying in terror about the barn.

THE FOX AND THE COCK

A fox one day met a cock, and they began talking.

'How many tricks canst thou do?' said the fox.

'Well,' said the cock, 'I could do three; how many canst thou do thyself?'

'I could do three score and thirteen,' said the fox.

'What tricks canst thou do?' said the cock.

'Well,' said the fox, 'my grandfather used to shut one eye and give a great shout.'

'I could do that myself,' said the cock.

'Do it,' said the fox. And the cock shut one eye and crowed as loud as ever he could, but he shut the eye that was next the fox, and the fox gripped him by the neck and ran away with him. But the wife to whom the cock belonged saw him and cried out, 'Let go the cock; he's mine.'

'Say thou, SE MO CHOILEACH FHEIN A TH' ANN' (it is my own cock), said the cock to the fox.

Then the fox opened his mouth to say as the cock did, and he dropped the cock, and he sprung up on the top of a house, and shut one eye and gave a loud crow; and that's all there is of that sgeulachd.[1]

HOW THE WOLF LOST HIS TAIL

One day the wolf and the fox were out together, and they stole a dish of crowdie. Now the wolf was the biggest beast of the two, and he had a long tail like a greyhound, and great teeth.

The fox was afraid of him, and did not dare to say a word when the wolf ate the most of the crowdie, and left only a little at the bottom of the dish for him, but he determined to punish him for it; so the next night when they were out together the fox said –

'I smell a very nice cheese, and' (pointing to the moonshine on the ice) 'there it is too.'

'And how will you get it?' said the wolf.

'Well, stop you here till I see if the farmer is asleep, and if you keep your tail on it, nobody will see you or know

[1]Tale.

that it is there. Keep it steady. I may be some time coming back.'

So the wolf lay down and laid his tail on the moonshine in the ice, and kept it for an hour till it was fast. Then the fox, who bad been watching him, ran in to the farmer and said: 'The wolf is there; he will eat up the children – the wolf! the wolf!'

Then the farmer and his wife came out with sticks to kill the wolf, but the wolf ran off leaving his tail behind him, and that's why the wolf is stumpy-tailed to this day, though the fox has a long brush.[1]

THE FROG AND THE CROW

Here is a bit of crow language – a conversation with a frog. When it is repeated in Gaelic it can be made absurdly like the notes of the creatures.

'Ghille Criosda mhic Dhughail cuir a nois do mhàg.'

Christ's servant, son of Dugald, put up thy paw.

'Tha eagal orm, tha eagal orm, tha eagal orm.'

I fear.

'Gheibh thu còta gorm a's léine. Gheibh thu còta gorm a's léine.'

Thou shalt have a blue coat and a shirt.

Then the frog put up his hand and the hoodie took him to a hillock and began to eat him, saying,

'Biadh dona lom! 's bu dona riabh thu.'

Bad bare meat and bad wert thou ever.

'Caite bheil do ghealladh math a nis?' said the frog.

Where is thy good promise now?

[1] The story errs in ascribing a stumpy tail to the wolf.

'Sann ag ol a bha sinn an latha sin. Sann ag ol a bha sinn an latha sin.'

It is drinking we were on that day.

'Toll ort a ruid ghrannda gur beag feola tha air do chramhan.'

'Toll ort!' said the hoodie.

A hole in thee, ugly thing! how little flesh is on thy bones.

THE GROUSE COCK AND HIS WIFE

The Grouse Cock and his wife are always disputing, and may be heard on any fine evening or early morning quarrelling and scolding about the stock of food.

This is what the hen says –

'FAIC THUSA 'N LA UD 'S AN LA UD EILE.'

And the cock, with his deeper voice, replies –

'FAIC THUSA 'N CNOC UD 'S AN CNOC UD EILE.'

See thou yonder day, and yon other day.

See thou yonder hill, and yon other hill.

THE EAGLE AND THE WREN[1]

The Eagle and the Wren once tried who could fly highest, and the victor was to be king of the birds. So the Wren flew straight up, and the Eagle flew in great circles, and when the Wren was tired he settled on the Eagle's back.

When the Eagle was tired he stopped, and –

'Where art thou, Wren?' said the Eagle.

'I am here above thee,' said the Wren.

And so the Wren won the match.

[1] This story describes the flight of eagle and wren correctly enough.

THE WREN'S PRESUMPTION

Thou'rt lessened by that, said the Wren, when he dipped his beak in the sea.

THE TWO FOXES

A man was one day walking along the road with a creel of herrings on his back, and two foxes saw him, and the one, who was the biggest, said to the other, 'Stop thou here, and follow the man, and I will run round and pretend that I am dead.' So he ran round, and stretched himself on the road. The man came on, and when he saw the fox, he was well pleased to find so fine a beast, and he picked him up, and threw him into the creel, and he walked on. But the fox threw the herrings out of the creel, and the other followed and picked them up; and when the creel was empty, the big fox leaped out and ran away, and that is how they got the herrings.

Well, they went on together till they came to a smith's house, and there was a horse tied at the door, and he had a golden shoe, and there was a name on it.

'I will go and read what is written on that shoe,' said the big fox, and he went; but the horse lifted his foot, and struck a kick on him, and drove his brains out.

'Lad, lad,' said the little fox, 'no scholar me, nor wish I to be;' and, of course, he got the herrings.

THE BEE AND THE MOUSE

A Bee met a mouse and said –
  'Come over till we make a house.'
      'I will not,' said Luchag, the mousie.
      'He to whom thou gavest thy summer honey,
      Let him make a winter house for thee;
      I have a little house under the ground,
      That can reach neither cold nor breeze,
      Thou wilt be a ragged creature,
      Running on the tops of the trees.'

THE TWO MICE

There was a mouse in the hill, and a mouse in a farm.

  'It were well,' said the hill mouse, 'to be in the farm, where one might get things.'

  Said the farm mouse, 'Better is peace.'

GIANTS AND MONSTERS

Giants and Monsters

THE BATTLE OF THE BIRDS*

There was once a time when every creature and bird was gathering to battle. The son of the king of Tethertown said that he would go to see the battle, and that he would bring sure word home to his father the king, who would be king of the creatures this year. The battle was over before he arrived all but one fight, between a great black raven and a snake, and it seemed as if the snake would get the victory over the raven. When the king's son saw this, he helped the raven, and with one blow he takes the head off the snake. When the raven had taken breath, and saw that the snake was dead, he said, 'For thy kindness to me this day I will give thee a sight. Come up now on the root of my two wings.' The king's son mounted upon the raven, and, before he stopped, he took him over seven Bens, and seven Glens, and seven Mountain Moors.

'Now,' said the raven, 'seest thou that house yonder? Go now to it. It is a sister of mine that makes her dwelling in it; and I will go bail that thou art welcome. And if she asks thee, Wert thou at the battle of the birds? say thou that thou wert. And if she asks, Didst thou see my

*J. F. Campbell, *Popular Tales of the West Highlands*.

likeness? say that thou sawest it. But be sure that thou meetest me tomorrow morning here, in this place.' The king's son got good and right good treatment this night. Meat of each meat, drink of each drink, warm water to his feet, and a soft bed for his limbs.

On the next day the raven gave him the same sight over seven Bens, and seven Glens, and seven Mountain Moors. They saw a bothy far off; but, though far off, they were soon there. He got good treatment this night, as before – plenty of meat and drink, and warm water to his feet, and a soft bed to his limbs – and on the next day it was the same thing.

On the third morning, instead of seeing the raven as at the other times, who should meet him but the handsomest lad he ever saw, with a bundle in his band. The king's son asked this lad if he had seen a big black raven. Said the lad to him, 'Thou wilt never see the raven again, for I am that raven. I was put under spells; it was meeting thee that loosed me, and for that thou art getting this bundle. Now,' said the lad, 'thou wilt turn back on the self-same steps, and thou wilt lie a night in each house, as thou wert before; but thy lot is not to loose the bundle which I gave thee, till thou art in the place where thou wouldst most wish to dwell.'

The king's son turned his back to the lad, and his face to his father's house; and he got lodging from the raven's sisters, just as he got it when going forward. When he was nearing his father's house he was going through a close wood. It seemed to him that the bundle was growing heavy, and he thought he would look what was in it.

When he loosed the bundle, it was not without aston-ishing himself. In a twinkling he sees the very grandest place he ever saw. A great castle, and an orchard about the castle, in which was every kind of fruit and herb. He stood full of wonder and regret for having loosed the bundle – it was not in his power to put it back again – and he would have wished this pretty place to be in the pretty little green hollow that was opposite his father's house; but, at one glance, he sees a great giant coming towards him.

'Bad's the place where thou hast built thy house, king's son,' says the giant. 'Yes, but it is not here I would wish it to be, though it happened to be here by mishap,' says the king's son. 'What's the reward thou wouldst give me for putting it back in the bundle as it was before?' 'What's the reward thou wouldst ask?' says the king's son. 'If thou wilt give me the first son thou hast when he is seven years of age,' says the giant. 'Thou wilt get that if I have a son,' said the king's son.

In a twinkling the giant put each garden, and orchard, and castle in the bundle as they were before. 'Now,' says the giant, 'take thou thine own road, and I will take my road; but mind thy promise, and though thou shouldst forget, I will remember.'

The king's son took to the road, and at the end of a few days he reached the place he was fondest of. He loosed the bundle, and the same place was just as it was before. And when he opened the castle door he sees the handsomest maiden he ever cast eye upon. 'Advance, king's son,' said the pretty maid; 'everything is in order for thee, if thou wilt marry me this very night.' 'It's I am the man that is willing,' said the king's son. And on the same night they married.

But at the end of a day and seven years, what great man is seen coming to the castle but the giant. The king's son minded his promise to the giant, and till now he had not told his promise to the queen. 'Leave thou the matter between me and the giant,' says the queen.

'Turn out thy son,' says the giant; 'mind your promise.' 'Thou wilt get that,' says the king, 'when his mother puts him in order for his journey.' The queen arrayed the cook's son, and she gave him to the giant by the hand. The giant went away with him; but he had not gone far when he put a rod in the hand of the little laddie. The giant asked him, 'If thy father had that rod, what would he do with it?' 'If my father had that rod he would beat the dogs and the cats, if they would be going near the king's meat,' said the little laddie. 'Thou'rt the cook's son,' said the giant. He catches him by the two small ankles and knocks him – 'Sgleog' – against the stone that was beside him. The giant turned back to the castle in rage and madness, and he said that if they did not turn out the king's son to him, the highest stone of the castle would be the lowest. Said the queen to the king, 'We'll try it yet; the butler's son is of the same age as our son.' She arrayed the butler's son, and she gives him to the giant by the hand. The giant had not gone far when he put the rod in his hand. 'If thy father had that rod,' said the giant, 'what would he do with it?' 'He would beat the dogs and cats when they would be coming near the king's bottles and glasses.' 'Thou art the son of the butler,' says the giant, and dashed his brains out too. The giant returned in very great rage and anger. The earth shook under the soles of his feet, and the castle shook and all that was in it. 'OUT HERE THY SON,' says the giant, 'or in a twinkling the stone that is highest in the dwelling will be the lowest.' So needs must they had to give the king's son to the giant.

The giant took him to his own house, and he reared him as his own son. On a day of days when the giant was from home, the lad heard the sweetest music he ever heard in a room at the top of the giant's house. At a glance he saw the finest face he had ever seen. She beckoned to him to come a bit nearer to her, and she told him to go this time, but to be sure to be at the same place about that dead midnight.

And as he promised he did. The giant's daughter was at his side in a twinkling, and she said, 'To-morrow thou wilt get the choice of my two sisters to marry; but say thou that thou wilt not take either, but me. My father wants me to marry the son of the king of the Green City, but I don't like him.' On the morrow the giant took out his three daughters, and he said, 'Now, son of the king of Tether-town, thou hast not lost by living with me so long. Thou wilt get to wife one of the two eldest of my daughters, and with her leave to go home with her the day after the wedding.' 'If thou wilt give me this pretty little one,' says the king's son, 'I will take thee at thy word.'

The giant's wrath kindled, and he said, 'Before thou gett'st her thou must do the three things that I ask thee to do.' 'Say on,' says the king's son. The giant took him to the byre. 'Now,' says the giant, 'the dung of a hundred cattle is here, and it has not been cleansed for seven years. I am going from home today, and if this byre is not cleaned before night comes, so clean that a golden apple will run from end to end of it, not only thou shalt not get my daughter, but 'tis a drink of thy blood that will quench my thirst this night.' He begins cleaning the byre, but it was just as well to keep baling the great ocean. After midday, when sweat was blinding him, the giant's young daughter came where he was, and she said to him, 'Thou art being punished, king's son.' 'I am that,' says the king's son. 'Come over,' says she, 'and lay down thy weariness.' 'I will do that,' says he, 'there is but death awaiting me, at any rate.' He sat down near her. He was so tired that he fell asleep beside her. When he awoke, the giant's daughter was not to be seen, but the byre was so well cleaned that a golden apple would run from end to end of it. In comes the giant, and he said, 'Thou hast cleaned the byre, king's son?' 'I have cleaned it,' says he. 'Somebody cleaned it,' says the giant. 'Thou didst not clean it, at all events,' said the king's son. 'Yes, yes,' says the giant, 'since thou wert so active today, thou wilt get to this time tomorrow to thatch this byre with birds' down – birds with no two feathers of one colour.' The king's son was on foot before the sun; he caught up his bow and his quiver of arrows to kill the birds. He took to the moors, but if he did, the birds were not so easy to take. He was running after them till the sweat was blinding him. About midday who should come but the giant's daughter. 'Thou art exhausting thyself, king's son,' says she. 'I am,' said he. 'There fell but these two black-birds, and both of one colour.' 'Come over and lay down thy weariness on this pretty hillock,' says the giant's daughter. 'It's I am willing,' says he. He thought she would aid him this time, too, and he sat down near her, and he was not long there till he fell asleep.

When he awoke, the giant's daughter was gone. He thought he would go back to the house, and he sees the byre thatched with the feathers. When the giant came home, he said, 'Thou hast thatched the byre, king's son?' 'I thatched it,' says he. 'Somebody thatched it,' says the giant. 'Thou didst not thatch it,' says the king's son. 'Yes, yes!' says the giant. 'Now,' says the giant, 'there is a fir-tree beside that loch down there, and there is a magpie's nest in its top. The eggs thou wilt find in the nest. I must have them for my first meal. Not one must be burst or broken, and there are five in the nest.' Early in the morning the king's son went where the tree was, and that tree was not hard to hit upon. Its match was not in the whole wood. From the foot to the first branch was five hundred feet. The king's son was going all round the tree. She came who was always bringing help to him; 'Thou art losing the skin of thy hands and feet.' 'Ach! I am,' says he. 'I am no sooner up than down.' 'This is no time for stopping,' says the giant's daughter. She thrust finger after finger into the tree, till she made a ladder for the king's son to go up to the magpie's nest. When he was at the nest, she said, 'Make haste now with the eggs, for my father's breath is burning my back.' In his hurry she left her little finger in the top of the tree. 'Now,' says she, 'thou wilt go home with the eggs quickly, and thou wilt get me to marry tonight if thou canst know me. I and my two sisters will be arrayed in the same garments, and made like each other, but look at me when my father says, "Go to thy wife, king's son"; and thou wilt see a hand without a little finger.' He gave the eggs to the giant. 'Yes, yes!' says the giant, 'be making ready for thy marriage.'

Then indeed there was a wedding, and it *was* a wedding! Giants and gentlemen, and the son of the king of the Green City was in the midst of them. They were married, and the dancing began, and that was a dance! The giant's house was shaking from top to bottom. But bed-time came, and the giant said, 'It is time for thee to go to rest, son of the king of Tethertown; take thy bride with thee from amidst those.'

She put out the hand off which the little finger was, and he caught her by the hand.

'Thou hast aimed well this time too; but there is no knowing but we may meet thee another way,' said the giant.

But to rest they went. 'Now,' says she, 'sleep not, or else

thou diest. We must fly quick, quick, or for certain my father will kill thee.'

Out they went, and on the blue grey filly in the stable they mounted. 'Stop a while,' says she, 'and I will play a trick to the old hero.' She jumped in, and cut an apple into nine shares, and she put two shares at the head of the bed, and two shares at the foot of the bed, and two shares at the door of the kitchen, and two shares at the big door, and one outside the house.

The giant awoke and called, 'Are you asleep?' 'We are not yet,' said the apple that was at the head of the bed. At the end of a while he called again. 'We are not yet,' said the apple that was at the foot of the bed. A while after this he called again. 'We are not yet,' said the apple at the kitchen door. The giant called again. The apple that was at the big door answered. 'You are now going far from me,' says the giant. 'We are not yet,' says the apple that was outside the house. 'You are flying,' says the giant. The giant jumped on his feet, and to the bed he went, but it was cold – empty.

'My own daughter's tricks are trying me,' said the giant. 'Here's after them,' says he.

In the mouth of day, the giant's daughter said that her father's breath was burning her back. 'Put thy hand, quick,' said she, 'in the ear of the grey filly, and whatever thou findest in it, throw it behind thee.' 'There is a twig of sloe tree,' said he. 'Throw it behind thee,' said she.

No sooner did he that than there were twenty miles of black-thorn wood, so thick that scarce a weasel could go through it. The giant came headlong, and there he is fleecing his head and neck in the thorns.

'My own daughter's tricks are here as before,' said the giant; 'but if I had my own big axe and wood knife here, I would not be long making a way through this.' He went home for the big axe and the wood knife, and sure he was not long on his journey, and he was the boy behind the big axe. He was not long making a way through the black thorn. 'I will leave the axe and the wood knife here till I return,' says he. 'If thou leave them,' said a hoodie that was in a tree, 'we will steal them.'

'You will do that same,' says the giant, 'but I will set them home.' He returned and left them at the house. At the heat of day the giant's daughter felt her father's breath burning her back.

'Put thy finger in the filly's ear, and throw behind thee whatever thou findest in it.' He got a splinter of grey stone, and in a twinkling there were twenty miles, by breadth and height, of great grey rock behind them. The giant came full pelt, but past the rock he could not go.

'The tricks of my own daughter are the hardest things that ever met me,' says the giant; 'but if I had my lever and my mighty mattock, I would not be long making my way through this rock also.' There was no help for it, but to turn the chase for them; and he was the boy to split the stones. He was not long making a road through the rock. 'I will leave the tools here, and I will return no more.' 'If thou leave them,' said the hoodie, 'we will steal them.' 'Do that if thou wilt; there is no time to go back.' At the time of breaking the watch, the giant's daughter said that she was feeling her father's breath burning her back. 'Look in the filly's ear, king's son, or else we are lost.' He did so, and it was a bladder of water that was in her ear this time. He threw it behind him and there was a freshwater loch, twenty miles in length and breadth, behind them.

The giant came on but with the speed he had on him, he

was in the middle of the loch, and he went under, and he rose no more.

On the next day the young companions were come in sight of his father's house. 'Now,' said she, 'my father is drowned, and he won't trouble us any more; but before we go any further,' says she, 'go thou to thy father's house, and tell that thou hast the like of me; but this is thy lot, let neither man nor creature kiss thee, for if thou dost thou wilt not remember that thou hast ever seen me.' Every one he met was giving him welcome and luck, and he charged his father and mother not to kiss him; but as mishap was to be, an old greyhound was in and she knew him, and jumped up to his mouth, and after that he did not remember the giant's daughter.

She was sitting at the well's side as he left her, but the king's son was not coming. In the mouth of night she climbed up into a tree of oak that was beside the well, and she lay in the fork of the tree all that night. A shoemaker had a house near the well, and about midday on the morrow the shoemaker asked his wife to go for a drink for him out of the well. When the shoemaker's wife reached the well, and when she saw the shadow of her that was in the tree, thinking of it that it was her own shadow – and she never thought till now that she was so handsome – she gave a cast to the dish that was in her hand, and it was broken on the ground, and she took herself to the house without vessel or water.

'Where is the water, wife?' said the shoemaker. 'Thou shambling, contemptible old carle, without grace, I have stayed too long thy water and wood thrall.' 'I am thinking, wife, that thou hast turned crazy. Go thou, daughter, quickly, and fetch a drink for thy father.' His daughter went, and in the same way so it happened to her. She never thought till now that she was so lovable, and she took herself home. 'Up with the drink,' said her father. 'Thou home-spun shoe carle, dost thou think that I am fit to be thy thrall.' The poor shoemaker thought that they had taken a turn in their understandings, and he went himself to the well. He saw the shadow of the maiden in the well, and he looked up to the tree, and he sees the finest woman he ever saw. 'Thy seat is wavering, but thy face is fair,' said the shoemaker. 'Come down, for there is need of thee for a short while at my house.' The shoemaker understood that this was the shadow that had driven his people mad. The shoemaker took her to his house, and he said that he had but a poor bothy, but that she should get a share of all that was in it. At the end of a day or two came a leash of gentlemen lads to the shoemaker's house for shoes to be made for them, for the king had come home, and he was going to marry. The glance the lads gave they saw the giant's daughter, and if they saw her, they never saw one so pretty as she. ''Tis thou hast the pretty daughter here,' said the lads to the shoemaker. 'She is pretty, indeed,' says the shoemaker, 'but she is no daughter of mine.' 'St Nail!' said one of them, 'I would give a hundred pounds to marry her.' The two others said the very same. The poor shoemaker said that he had nothing to do with her. 'But,' said they, 'ask her tonight, and send us word tomorrow.' When the gentles went away, she asked the shoemaker, 'What's that they were saying about me?' The shoemaker told her. 'Go thou after them,' said she; 'I will marry one of them, and let him bring his purse with him.' The youth returned, and he gave the shoemaker a hundred pounds for tocher. They went to rest, and when she had laid down, she asked the lad for a drink of water from a tumbler that was on the board on the further side of the chamber. He went; but out of that he could not come, as he held the vessel of water the length of the night. 'Thou lad,' said she, 'why wilt thou not lie down?' but out of that he could not drag till the bright morrow's day was. The shoemaker came to the door of the chamber, and she asked him to take away that lubberly boy. This wooer went and betook himself to his home, but he did not tell the other two how it happened to him. Next came the second chap, and in the same way, when she had gone to rest, 'Look,' she said, 'if the latch is on the door.' The latch laid hold of his hands, and out of that he could not come the length of the night, and out of that he did not come till the morrow's day was bright. He went, under shame and disgrace. No matter, he did not tell the other chap how it had happened, and on the third night he came. As it happened to the two others, so it happened to him. One foot stuck to the floor; he could neither come nor go, but so he was the length of the night. On the morrow, he took his soles out of that, and he was not seen looking behind him. 'Now,' said the girl to the shoemaker, 'thine is the sporran of gold; I have no need of it. It will better thee, and I am no worse for thy kindness to me.' The shoemaker had the shoes ready, and on that very day the king was to be married. The shoemaker was going to the castle with the shoes of the young people, and the girl said to the shoemaker, 'I would like to get a sight of the king's son before he marries.' 'Come with me,'says the shoemaker. 'I am well acquainted with the servants of the castle, and thou shalt get a sight of the king's son and all the company.' And when the gentles saw the pretty woman that was here they took her to the wedding-room, and they filled for her a glass of wine. When she was going to drink what is in it, a flame went up out of the glass, and a golden pigeon and a silver pigeon sprung out of it. They were flying about when three grains of barley fell on the floor. The silver pigeon sprang, and he eats that. Said the golden pigeon to him, 'If thou hadst mind when I cleared the byre, thou wouldst not eat that without giving me a share.' Again fell three other grains of barley, and the silver pigeon sprang, and he eats that, as before. "If thou hadst mind when I thatched the byre, thou wouldst not eat that without giving me my share,' says the golden pigeon. Three other grains fall, and the silver pigeon sprang, and he eats that. 'If thou hadst mind when I harried the magpie's nest, thou wouldst not eat that without giving me my share,' says the golden pigeon; 'I lost my little finger bringing it down, and I want it still.' The king's son minded, and he knew who it was he had got. He sprang where she was, and kissed her from hand to mouth. And when the priest came they married a second time. And there I left them.

THE SEA-MAIDEN*

There was ere now a poor old fisher, but on this year he was not getting much fish. On a day of days, and he fishing, there rose a sea-maiden at the side of his boat, and she asked him if he was getting fish. The old man answered, and he said that he was not. 'What reward wouldst thou give me for sending plenty of fish to thee?' 'Ach!' said the old man, 'I have not much to spare.' 'Wilt thou give me the first son thou hast?' said she. 'It is I that would give thee that, if I were to have a son; there was not, and there will not be a son of mine,' said he, 'I and my wife are grown so old.' 'Name all thou hast.' 'I have but an old

*Campbell, *Popular Tales of the West Highlands.*

mare of a horse, an old dog, myself, and my wife. There's for thee all the creatures of the great world that are mine.' 'Here, then, are three grains for thee that thou shalt give thy wife this very night, and three others to the dog, and these three to the mare, and these three likewise thou shalt plant behind thy house, and in their own time thy wife will have three sons, the mare three foals, and the dog three puppies, and there will grow three trees behind thy house, and the trees will be a sign, when one of the sons dies, one of the trees will wither. Now, take thyself home, and remember me when thy son is three years of age, and thou thyself wilt get plenty of fish after this.' Everything happened as the sea-maiden said, and he himself was getting plenty of fish; but when the end of the three years was nearing, the old man was growing sorrowful, heavy-hearted, while he failed each day as it came. On the name-sake of the day, he went to fish as he used, but he did not take his son with him.

The sea-maiden rose at the side of the boat, and asked, 'Didst thou bring thy son with thee hither to me?' 'Och! I did not bring him. I forgot that this was the day.' 'Yes! yes! then,' said the sea-maiden; 'thou shalt get four other years of him, to try if it be easier for thee to part from him. Here thou hast his like age,' and she lifted up a big bouncing baby. 'Is thy son as fine as this one?' He went home full of glee and delight, for that he had got four other years of his son, and he kept on fishing and getting plenty of fish, but at the end of the next four years sorrow and woe struck him, and he took not a meal, and he did not a turn, and his wife could not think what was ailing him. This time he did not know what to do, but he set it before him, that he would not take his son with him this time either. He went to fish as at the former times, and the sea-maiden rose at the side of the boat, and she asked him, 'Didst thou bring thy son hither to me?' 'Och! I forgot him this time too,' said the old man. 'Go home, then,' said the sea-maiden, 'and at the end of seven years after this thou art sure to remember me; but then it will not be the easier for thee to part with him, but thou shalt get fish as thou used to do.'

The old man went home full of joy; he had got seven other years of his son, and before seven years passed, the old man thought that he himself would be dead, and that he would see the sea-maiden no more. But no matter, the end of those seven years was nearing also, and if it was, the old man was not without care and trouble. He had rest neither day nor night. The eldest son asked his father one day if any one were troubling him. The old man said that some one was, but that belonged neither to him nor to any one else. The lad said he *must* know what it was. His father told him at last how the matter was between him and the sea-maiden. 'Let not that put you in any trouble,' said the son; 'I will not oppose you.' 'Thou shalt not; thou shalt not go, my son, though I should not get fish for ever.' 'If you will not let me go with you, go to the smithy, and let the smith make me a great strong sword, and I will go to the end of fortune.' His father went to the smithy, and the smith made a doughty sword for him. His father came home with the sword. The lad grasped it and gave it a shake or two, and it went in a hundred splinters. He asked his father to go to the smithy and get him another sword, in which there should be twice as much weight; and so did his father, and so likewise it happened to the next sword – it broke in two halves. Back went the old man to the smithy; and the smith made a great sword, its like he never made before. 'There's thy sword for thee,' said the smith, 'and the fist must be good that plays this blade.' The old man gave the sword to his son, he gave it a shake or two. 'This will do,' said he; 'it's high time now to travel on my way.' On the next morning he put a saddle on the black horse that the mare had, and he put the world under his head,[1] and his black dog was by his side. When he went on a bit, he fell in with the carcase of a sheep beside the road. At the carrion were a great dog, a falcon, and an otter. He came down off the horse, and he divided the carcase amongst the three. Three third shares to the dog, two third shares to the otter, and a third share to the falcon. 'For this,' said the dog, 'if swiftness of foot or sharpness of tooth will give thee aid, mind me, and I will be at thy side.' Said the otter, 'If the swimming of foot on the ground of a pool will loose thee, mind me, and I will be at thy side.' Said the falcon, 'If hardship comes on thee, where swiftness of wing or crook of a claw will do good, mind me, and I will be at thy side.' On this he went onward till he reached a king's house, and he took service to be a herd, and his wages were to be according to the milk of the cattle. He went away with the cattle, and the grazing was but bare. In the evening, when he took them home, they had not much milk, the place was so bare, and his meat and drink was but spare this night.

On the next day he went on further with them; and at last he came to a place exceedingly grassy, in a green glen, of which he never saw the like.

But about the time when he should go behind the cattle, for taking homewards, who is seen coming but a great giant with his sword in his hand. 'HIU! HAU!! HOGARAICH!!!' says the giant. 'It is long since my teeth were rusted seeking thy flesh. The cattle are mine; they are on my march; and a

[1] Took the world for his pillow.

dead man art thou.' 'I said not that,' says the herd; 'there is no knowing, but that may be easier to say than to do.'

To grips they go – himself and the giant. He saw that he was far from his friend, and near his foe. He drew the great clean-sweeping sword, and he neared the giant; and in the play of the battle the black dog leaped on the giant's back. The herd drew back his sword, and the head was off the giant in a twinkling. He leaped on the black horse, and he went to look for the giant's house. He reached a door, and in the haste that the giant made he had left each gate and door open. In went the herd, and that's the place where there was magnificence and money in plenty, and dresses of each kind on the wardrobe with gold and silver, and each thing finer than the other. At the mouth of night he took himself to the king's house, but he took not a thing from the giant's house. And when the cattle were milked this night there *was* milk. He got good feeding this night, meat and drink without stint, and the king was hugely pleased that he had caught such a herd. He went for a time in this way, but at last the glen grew bare of grass, and the grazing was not so good.

But he thought he would go a little further forward in on the giant's land; and he sees a great park of grass. He returned for the cattle, and he puts them into the park.

They were but a short time grazing in the park when a great wild giant came full of rage and madness. 'Hiu! Hau!! Hogaraich!!!' said the giant. 'It is a drink of thy blood that quenches my thirst this night.' 'There is no knowing,' said the herd, 'but that's easier to say than to do.' And at each other went the men. *There* was the shaking of blades! At length and at last it seemed as if the giant would get the victory over the herd. Then he called on his dog, and with one spring the black dog caught the giant by the neck, and swiftly the herd struck off his head.

He went home very tired this night, but it's a wonder if the king's cattle had not milk. The whole family was delighted that they had got such a herd.

He followed herding in this way for a time; but one night after he came home, instead of getting 'all hail' and 'good luck' from the dairymaid, all were at crying and woe.

He asked what cause of woe there was that night. The dairymaid said that a great beast with three heads was in the loch, and she was to get some one every year, and the lots had come this year on the king's daughter, 'and in the middle of the day tomorrow she is to meet the Uile Bheist at the upper end of the loch, but there is a great suitor yonder who is going to rescue her.'

'What suitor is that?' said the herd. 'Oh, he is a great General of arms,' said the dairymaid, 'and when he kills the beast, he will marry the king's daughter, for the king has said that he who could save his daughter should get her to marry.'

But on the morrow when the time was nearing, the king's daughter and this hero of arms went to give a meeting to the beast, and they reached the black corrie at the upper end of the loch. They were but a short time there when the beast stirred in the midst of the loch; but on the General's seeing this terror of a beast with three heads, he took fright, and he slunk away, and he hid himself. And the king's daughter was under fear and under trembling with no one at all to save her. At a glance, she sees a doughty handsome youth, riding a black horse, and coming where she was. He was marvellously arrayed, and full armed, and his black dog moving after him. 'There is gloom on thy fair face, girl,' said the youth. 'What dost thou here?' 'Oh! that's no matter,' said the king's daughter. 'It's not long I'll be

here at all events.' 'I said not that,' said he. 'A worthy
fled as likely as thou, and not long since,' said she. 'He is a
worthy who stands the war,' said the youth. He lay down
beside her, and he said to her, if he should fall asleep, she
should rouse him when she should see the beast making for
shore. 'What is rousing for thee?' said she. 'Rousing for
me is to put the gold ring on thy finger on my little finger.'
They were not long there when she saw the beast making
for the shore. She took a ring off her finger, and put it on
the little finger of the lad. He awoke, and to meet the beast
he went with his sword and his dog. But there was the
spluttering and splashing between himself and the beast!
The dog was doing all he might, and the king's daughter
was palsied by fear of the noise of the beast. They would
now be under, and now above. But at last he cut one of the
heads off her. She gave one roar RAIVIC, and the son of
earth, MACTALLA of the rocks (echo), called to her screech,
and she drove the loch in spindrift from end to end, and in
a twinkling she went out of sight. 'Good luck and victory
that were following thee, lad!' said the king's daughter. 'I
am safe for one night, but the beast will come again, and
for ever, until the other two heads come off her.' He
caught the beast's head, and he drew a withy through it,
and he told her to bring it with her there tomorrow. She
went home with the head on her shoulder, and the herd
betook himself to the cows; but she had not gone far when
this great General saw her, and he said to her that he would
kill her, if she would not say that 'twas he took the head off
the beast. 'Oh!' says she, ''tis I will say it, Who else took
the head off the beast but thou!' They reached the king's
house, and the head was on the General's shoulder. But
here was rejoicing, that she should come home alive and
whole, and this great captain with the beast's head full of

blood in his hand. On the morrow they went away, and there was no question at all but that this hero would save the king's daughter.

They reached the same place, and they were not long there when the fearful Uile Bheist stirred in the midst of the loch, and the hero slunk away as he did on yesterday, but it was not long after this when the man of the black horse came with another dress on. No matter, she knew it was the very same lad. 'It is I am pleased to see thee,' said she. 'I am in hopes thou wilt handle thy great sword today as thou didst yesterday. Come up and take breath.' But they were not long there when they saw the beast steaming in the midst of the loch.

The lad lay down at the side of the king's daughter, and he said to her, 'If I sleep before the beast comes, rouse me.' 'What is rousing for thee?' 'Rousing for me is to put the ear-ring that is in thine ear in mine.' He had not well fallen asleep when the king's daughter cried, 'Rouse! rouse!' but wake he would not; but she took the ear-ring out of her ear, and she put it in the ear of the lad. At once he woke, and to meet the beast he went, but *there* was Tloopersteich and Tlaperstich, rawceil s'tawceil, spluttering, splashing, raving, and roaring on the beast! They kept on thus for a long time, and about the mouth of night, he cut another head off the beast. He put it on the withy, and he leaped on the black horse, and be betook himself to the herding. The king's daughter went home with the heads. The General met her, and took the heads from her, and he said to her, that she must tell that it was he who took the head off the beast this time also. 'Who else took the head off the beast but thou?' said she. They reached the king's house with the heads. Then there was joy and gladness. If the king was hopeful the first night, he was now sure that this great hero would save his daughter, and there was no question at all but that the other head would be off the beast on the morrow.

About the same time on the morrow the two went away. The officer hid himself as he usually did. The king's daughter betook herself to the bank of the loch. The hero of the black horse came, and he lay at her side. She woke the lad, and put another ear-ring in his other ear; and at the beast he went. But if rawceil and toiceil, roaring and raving, were on the beast on the days that were passed, this day she was horrible. But no matter, he took the third head off the beast; and if he did, it was not without a struggle. He drew it through the withy, and she went home with the heads. When they reached the king's house, all were full of smiles, and the General was to marry the king's daughter the next day. The wedding was going on, and every one about the castle longing till the priest should come. But when the priest came, she would marry but the one who could take the heads off the withy without cutting the withy. 'Who should take the heads off the withy but the man that put the heads on?' said the king.

The General tried them, but he could not loose them; and at last there was no one about the house but had tried to take the heads off the withy, but they could not. The king asked if there were any one else about the house that would try to take the heads off the withy? They said that the herd had not tried them yet. Word went for the herd and he was not long throwing them hither and thither. 'But stop a bit, my lad,' said the king's daughter; 'the man that took the heads off the beast, he has my ring and my two ear-rings.' The herd put his hand in his pocket, and he threw them on the board. 'Thou art my man,' said the king's daughter. The king was not so pleased when he saw that it was a herd who was to marry his daughter, but he ordered that he should be put in a better dress; but his daughter spoke, and she said that he had a dress as fine as any that ever was in his castle; and thus it happened. The herd put on the giant's golden dress, and they married that same night.

They were now married, and everything going on well. They were one day sauntering by the side of the loch, and there came a beast more wonderfully terrible than the other, and takes him away to the loch without fear, or asking. The king's daughter was now mournful, tearful, blind-sorrowful for her married man; she was always with her eye on the loch. An old smith met her, and she told how it had befallen her married mate. The smith advised her to spread everything that was finer than another in the very same place where the beast took away her man; and so she did. The beast put up her nose, and she said, 'Fine is thy jewellery, king's daughter.' 'Finer than that is the jewel that thou tookest from me,' said she. 'Give me one sight of my man, and thou shalt get any one thing of all these thou seest.' The beast brought him up. 'Deliver him to me, and thou shalt get all thou seest,' said she. The beast did as she said. She threw him alive and whole on the bank of the loch.

A short time after this, when they were walking at the side of the loch, the same beast took away the king's daughter. Sorrowful was each one that was in the town on this night. Her man was mournful, tearful, wandering down and up about the banks of the loch, by day and night. The old smith met him. The smith told him that there was no way of killing the Uile Bheist but the one way, and this is it – 'In the island that is in the midst of the loch is Eillid Chaisfhion – the white-footed hind, of the slenderest legs, and the swiftest step, and though she should be caught, there would spring a hoodie out of her, and though the hoodie should be caught, there would spring a trout out of her, but there is an egg in the mouth of the trout, and the soul of the beast is in the egg, and if the egg breaks, the beast is dead.'

Now there was no way of getting to this island, for the beast would sink each boat and raft that would go on the loch. He thought he would try to leap the strait with the black horse, and even so he did. The black horse leaped the strait, and the black dog with one bound after him. He saw the Eillid, and he let the black dog after her, but when the black dog would be on one side of the island, the Eillid would be on the other side. 'Oh! good were now the great dog of the carcase of flesh here!' No sooner spoke he the word than the generous dog was at his side; and after the Eillid he took, and the worthies were not long in bringing her to earth. But he no sooner caught her than a hoodie sprang out of her. ''Tis now were good the falcon grey, of sharpest eye and swiftest wing!' No sooner said he this than the falcon was after the hoodie, and she was not long putting her to earth; and as the hoodie fell on the bank of the loch, out of her jumps the trout. 'Oh, that thou wert by me now, oh otter!' No sooner said than the otter was at his side, and out on the loch she leaped, and brings the trout from the midst of the loch; but no sooner was the otter on shore with the trout than the egg came from his mouth. He sprang and he put his foot on it. 'Twas then the beast let out a roar, and she said, 'Break not the egg, and thou gettest all thou askest.' 'Deliver to me my wife!' In the wink of an eye she was by his side. When he got hold of her hand in both his hands he let his foot down on the egg, and the beast died.

The beast was dead now, and now was the sight to be seen. She was horrible to look upon. The three heads were off her doubtless, but if they were, there were heads under and heads over head on her, and eyes, and five hundred feet. But no matter, they left her there, and they went home, and there was delight and smiling in the king's house that night. And till now he had not told the king how he killed the giants. The king put great honour on him, and he was a great man with the king.

Himself and his wife were walking one day, when he notced a little castle beside the loch in a wood; he asked his wife who was dwelling in it? She said that no one would be going near that castle, for that no one had yet come back to tell the tale who had gone there.

'The matter must not be so,' said he; 'this very night I will see who is dwelling in it.' 'Go not, go not,' said she; 'there never went man to this castle that returned.' 'Be that as it pleases,' says he. He went; he betakes himself to the castle. When he reached the door, a little flattering crone met him, standing in the door. 'All hail and good luck to thee, fisher's son; 'tis I myself am pleased to see thee; great is the honour for this kingdom, thy like to be come into it – thy coming in is fame for this little bothy; go in first; honour to the gentles; go on, and take breath.' In he went, but as he was going up, she drew the Slachdan druidhach on him, on the back of his head, and at once – there he fell.

On this night there was woe in the king's castle, and on the morrow there was a wail in the fisher's house. The tree is seen withering, and the fisher's middle son said that his brother was dead, and he made a vow and oath that he would go, and that he would know where the corpse of his brother was lying. He put saddle on a black horse, and rode after his black dog (for the three sons of the fisher had a black horse and a black dog); and without going hither or thither he followed on his brother's step till he reached the king's house.

This one was so like his elder brother, that the king's daughter thought it was her own man. He stayed in the castle. They told him how it befell his brother; and to the little castle of the crone go he must – happen hard or soft as it might. To the castle he went; and just as befell the eldest brother, so in each way it befell the middle son, and with one blow of the Slachdan druidhach the crone felled him stretched beside his brother.

On seeing the second tree withering, the fisher's youngest son said that now his two brothers were dead, and that he must know what death had come on them. On the black horse he went, and he followed the dog as his brothers did, and he hit the king's house before he stopped. 'Twas the king who was pleased to see him; but to the black castle (for that was its name) they would not let him go. But to the castle he must go; and so he reached the castle. 'All hail and good luck to thyself, fisher's son; 'tis I am pleased to see thee; go in and take breath,' said the crone. 'In before me, thou crone; I don't like flattery out of doors; go in and let's hear thy speech.' In went the crone, and when her back was to him he drew his sword and whips her head off; but the sword flew out of his hand. And swift the crone gripped her head with both hands, and puts it on her neck as it was before. The dog sprung on the crone, and she struck the generous dog with the club of magic; and there he lay. But this went not to make the youth more sluggish. To grips with the crone he goes; he got a hold of the Slachdan druidhach, and with one blow on the top of the head, she was on earth in the wink of an eye. He went forward, up a little, and he sees his two brothers lying side by side. He gave a blow to each one with the Slachdan druidhach, and on foot they were, and there was the spoil! Gold and silver, and each thing more precious than another, in the crone's castle. They came back to the king's house, and then there was rejoicing! The king was growing old. The eldest son of the fisherman was crowned king, and the pair of brothers stayed a day and a year in the king's house, and then the two went on their journey home, with the gold and silver of the crone, and each other grand thing which the king gave them; and if they have not died since then, they are alive to this very day.

ASSIPATTLE[1] AND THE MESTER STOORWORM *[2]

The goodman of Leegarth was a well-to-do Udaler, who lived on and farmed his own land. His farm lay in a valley, watered by a burn, and sheltered by surrounding hills. His goodwife was a thrifty and active housewife. She bore him seven sons and one daughter. The youngest son was called Assipattle. Now his brothers looked down upon Assipattle, and treated him with contempt. And perhaps this was natural, for he did little or no work on the farm. He ran about the doors and over the bridge-stones all day, in ragged clothes and uncombed hair, from which every breath of wind blew a puff of ashes. And in the evenings he would lie wallowing in the ashes. Assipattle had to sweep the floor, bring peats to the fire, and do any other little job too degrading for his elder brothers. His brothers cuffed and kicked him; the women laughed at him; so that he had

*Mr. W. Traill Dennison's MS.
[1]*Vide* Notes (page 299).

but a dog's life. And most folk thought he deserved no better. But his sister was kind to him. She would listen to his long stories, about trolls and giants, and encourage him to tell more; while his brothers would throw clods at him, and order him to stop his lying tales. What made his stories more provoking to his brothers was that he himself was always the great man in his tales, and was sure to come off on the winning side.

It fell on a day that the king's messengers came to Leegarth with a message to the goodman from the king. The king asked the goodman to send his daughter to live in the king's house, and be maid to the princess, the king's only child. So the damsel was dressed in her best; and with his own hands her father made her a pair of rivlins,[3] to wear in the king's house. And of them she was proud, because she had always gone bare-footed before. The lass was set on a pony, and sent to the princess. And after that Assipattle was more silent and dull than before.

Now it fell out that doleful tidings came to that part of the country. It was said that the Stoorworm was drawing near the land. And this news made the boldest heart beat faster. And, truly, the Stoorworm came, and set up his head to the land. He turned his awful mouth landward; and yawned horridly; so that when his jaws came together they made a noise that shook the earth and the sea. And this he did to show that, if not fed, he would consume the land. Now, you must know that this was the largest, the first, and the father of all the Stoorworms. Therefore was he well named the Mester Stoorworm. With his venomous breath he could kill every living creature on which it fell, and could wither up everything that grew. Fear fell on every heart, and there was lamentation in the land. Now, there was a mighty sorcerer in the kingdom, who was said to know all things. But the king loved not the sorcerer, thinking him a deceitful man. When the king and the Thing[4] had taken counsel for three days, and could find no plan by which they might escape the Stoorworm, or turn him from the land, and when the Thing had come to its wits' end, the queen came in to the Thing. She was a stern, bold wife, and very big and manlike withal, and she said to the Thing-men, 'Ye are all brave men and great warriors, when ye have only men to face. But now ye deal with a foe that laughs at your strength, and before him your weapons are straw. It is not by sword and spear, but by the power of sorcery, that this monster can be overcome. Take counsel with the great sorcerer, who knows all things; for wisdom wins where strength fails.' To her counsel they all agreed. So the sorcerer was called, and asked to give counsel. He was grisly and bokie[5] like. He said the question was a great one, and hard to be answered; yet would he give them counsel by sunrise on the following day. On that day the sorcerer told the Thing-men that the only way to satisfy the Stoorworm, and to save the land, was to feed him once a week with seven virgins. If this does not suffice, and soon remove the monster, there is only one remedy to save us. That remedy is so horrid that it may not be uttered unless the first plan fails. So spake the sorcerer. And his counsel was law; and so was it doomed. Every Saturday seven damsels were bound and laid on a rock in front of the monster. And he would stretch forth his terrible tongue, and sweep the lasses into his horrid mouth. It was a pitiful and heart-grieving sight to see the maidens, young and bonnie, devoured by the merciless monster.

Now it fell on a day that the folk about Leegarth went up to the top of a hill where they might see the Stoorworm; and they saw him devour his Saturday feast. To see that sight women wept and screamed. Strong men groaned, and their faces grew grey as cold ashes. While all lamented and wondered if there was no other way of saving the land, Assipattle stood up, staring at the Stoorworm with both eyes. And says he, 'I'm not afraid; I would willingly fight the great monster.' With that, his eldest brother gave Assipattle a kick, and bade him go home to the ash-hole. And as the sons of Leegarth went home together, Assipattle persisted in saying that he would kill the Stoorworm. Then his brothers were so provoked by his bragging, that they pelted him with stones, till he ran away. At night, the good-wife of Leegarth sent Assipattle into the barn, with a message for his brothers to come to supper. The brothers were threshing the supper straw for the cattle. His brothers threw Assipattle on the barn floor, heaped straw on the top of him, and would have smothered him had not his father come, and delivered him out of their hands. At supper, when the father was quarrelling with his sons for what they did in the barn, Assipattle said to his father, 'You needed not to have come to my help; for I could have fought them all, and would have beat every one of them had I wished.' Then they all laughed, and said, 'Why did you not try?' 'I wanted to save my strength,' said Assipattle, 'until I fight the Stoorworm.' Then all roared with laughter. And his father said, 'You'll fight the Stoorworm when I make spoons from the horns of the moon!'

Now there arose great murmuring and lamentation over all the land about the death of so many young damsels. Folk said, if this goes on, there will not be a woman to bring forth men left in the land. So the Thing was called, and the Thing-men called for the sorcerer, and demanded to know what was his second remedy. The sorcerer raised his ill-favoured form, his beard hanging down to his knees,

and his hair hanging around him like a mantle, and he said,
'With cruel sorrow do I say it, but there is only one remedy.
Oh, that I had never been born, or lived to see the day on
which I have to tell this remedy! The king's daughter, the
Princess Gemdelovely must be given to the Stoorworm.
Then shall the monster leave our land.' There was then
great silence in the Thing. At last the king arose, tall, grim,
and sorrowful. He said, 'She is my only child. She is my
dearest on earth. She should be my heir. Yet, if her death
can save the land, let her die. It beseems her well that the
last of the oldest race in the land should die for her folk.'
Then the Lawman[6] asked if this was the doom of the Thing.
None spoke, yet all held up their hands in approval. They
did so in sorrow, for Gemdelovely was beloved by all the
folk. When the Lawman, with sore heart, was about to rise,
the king's Kemperman[7] arose and said, 'I ask that this
doom, like other beasts, should have a tail. And that the tail
shall be, if after devouring the dear princess the monster
departeth not, then the sorcerer shall be the next diet of the
Stoorworm.' This was hailed with a shout of approval.

Before doom was said, the king asked a respite of three
weeks, that he might offer his daughter to any champion
that would fight the Stoorworm. This was granted; then the
Lawman spake the doom accordingly.

Then the king sent messengers to all the neighbouring
kingdoms, to tell all men that whosoever would by war or
craft remove the Stoorworm from the land should have
Gemdelovely for his wife, and with her the kingdom to
which she was heir, and the famous sword Sickersnapper.[8]
And that was the sword with which the renowned Oddie[9]
fought his foes, and drove them to the back side of the
world. Many a prince and great warrior thought this three-
fold prize the three greatest blessings on earth – a wife, a

kingdom, and a sword. But the danger of winning them made the heart of the boldest stand still.

When the goodman of Leegarth came from the Thing with this news, that the beautiful Gemdelovely was to be given to the monster, there was great lamentation made; for she was beloved of all except the queen, who was her stepmother. But Assipattle, whatever he thought, said nothing.

Now six-and-thirty great champions came to the king's house, hoping to win the prize. But when they looked on the Stoorworm, twelve of them fell sick, and were carried home. Twelve were so terrified that they ran home to their own countries. And twelve stayed at the king's house with their hearts in their stomachs.

On the evening before the great day, the king made to his men, and the twelve champions who abode with him, a great supper. It was a dreary feast – little eaten, and less said. And albeit the men drank deep, they had no spirit to make fun; for, you see, the dool of the morrow lay heavy on their hearts. And the king turned the back of the lamp[10] to himself that night.

When all but the king and his Kemperman had gone to bed, the king opened the great chest on which he sat. It was the high seat in the hall, in which his precious things were kept. The king took out the great sword Sickersnapper. 'Why take ye out Sickersnapper?' said the Kemperman; 'my lord, four-score and sixteen years will it be the morrow since you came into the world. And many a doughty deed have ye done in your time; but your day for fight is gone. Let Sickersnapper lie, my good lord; ye are too old to wield her[11] now.' 'Wheest!' said the king, 'or I'll try my strength on thy body. Thinkest thou that I, who have the great Oddie for my forebear, would abide to see my only bairn devoured by a monster and not strike a blow for my own flesh and blood? I tell thee – and with my thumbs crossed on the edge of Sickersnapper I swear it – that I and this good sword shall perish before my daughter die. Yes, dear Sickersnapper! Thou shalt draw blood from the Stoorworm ere he tastes the blood of an Oddie. And now, my trusty Kemper, hie thee to the shore by cock-crow. Prepare my boat, with mast up, and sail ready to hoist, and with her bow seaward. And see thou guard her till I come. It is the last service thou wilt do for me. Goodnight, old comrade!' And while the Kemperman stood with a tear in each eye, the king's rhymer, who lay on a bench pretending to be asleep, jumped up and made for the door. And as he reached the door, he sang in a doleful voice –

> 'Whar' fire brunt, is ammers cald;
> The man that ance wus bright an' bald
> Is noo unfeerdie, duff an' auld,
> An' cinno Sickersnapper wald.
> A slockid cinder an' cald ass
> Can niver save the bonnie lass.'[12]

The king threw a cog at the rhymer's head, but he was too quick for the ale cog. So that was the way the supper ended.

Now at Leegarth that night were great preparations; for all were to go on the morrow to witness the death of Gemdelovely. All were to go but Assipattle, who had to stay at home and herd the geese. And as he lay that night in the ashes, he could not sleep, being troubled with thought. And as he lay, he heard his father and mother discoursing in bed. Says the goodwife, 'You are all going to see the princess eaten tomorrow.' 'Indeed, goodwife, thou'll come with us tomorrow,' says the goodman. Says the goodwife,

'I do not think I will. I'm not able to go on my feet, and I do not care now to ride alone.' 'Thou needest not ride alone,' says the goodman; 'I'll take thee behind me, and we'll both ride on Teetgong;[13] and I'll be bound there will none go before us while we ride on him.' Now Teetgong was the fastest horse in all the land. Then quoth the good-wife, 'Why wouldst thou care to take an old wife like me behind thee before all the folk?' 'What havers!' said the goodman. 'Does thou think there is any one in the world I would like better to sit behind me than my ain goodwife?' 'I do not know,' says the goodwife; 'but I have sometimes thought thou did not love me as a husband should love his wife.' 'What puts such a notion in thy head?' said the goodman; 'thou knows I love thee better than any woman on earth. What did I ever do or say to make thee think I did not love thee?' 'It is not what thou sayest, it's what thou wilt not say, that makes me doubt thee. For the last five years I have lain at thee to tell me how thou makest Teetgong run so fast that he beats every other horse in the land; but I might as well ask the stone in the wall. Is that a sign of true love?' 'Indeed, goodwife,' said the goodman, 'maybe it was want of trust, but not want of love. For thou seest we men-folk think the women have a leak in their mind somewhere, maybe in the tongue; so I thought best to keep to myself what might hurt me in telling, but could not hurt thee by not knowing. But this shall not be a heart-vexer to thee any longer – I shall tell thee the whole secret. When I want Teetgong to stand, I give him a clap on the left shoulder; when I want him to ride fairly fast, I give him two claps on the right. And when I want him to run full speed, I blow through the wind-pipe of a goose. I aye keep the goose thrapple in the right-hand pouch of my coat, to be handy. And when Teetgong hears that, he goes swift as a storm of wind. So, now thou knowest all, keep thy mind at ease, and let us sleep, for it is late.'

Assipattle heard all this, and lay quiet as a mouse till he heard the old folk snoring. He did not rest long then, I can tell you. He pulled the wind-pipe of the goose out of his father's pocket, and slipped to the stable like a thief. He bridled Teetgong and led him out. There the horse pranced and reared madly, knowing he was not held by his own master. Assipattle clapped his hand on Teetgong's left shoulder; then the horse stood like a rock. Assipattle jumped on his back and clapped his right shoulder. So away they went. But, when starting, the horse gave a loud, loud neigh. This neigh awoke the goodman, for he knew the cry of his horse; he sprang up, aroused his sons, and all mounted and galloped after Teetgong, crying, thief! The goodman, who was foremost in the pursuit, roared –

> 'Hie, hie! ho!
> Teetgong, wo!'

And when Teetgong heard that, he stood stock still. Assipattle out with the goose thrapple, and blew with all his might. When Teetgong heard that, he went off like the wind, so that Assipattle could scarcely hold his breath. And the goodman and his sons returned home in doleful dumps for the loss of Teetgong.

Assipattle came near the shore as day began to light in the east. He came to a valley, and there tethered his horse; he had rolled the tether loosely round the neck of the horse. He walked till he came to a little house, where an old woman lay asleep. Here he found an old pot, in which he placed a live peat from the rested fire. And with pot and peat he went to the shore. There he saw the king's boat afloat, fastened to a stone on the beach. In the boat sat the man whose duty it was to watch till the king came. 'A nippie morning,' says Assipattle to the man. 'I think I may know that,' said the man. 'I have sitten here all night, till the very marrow of my bones is sturtened.'[14] 'Why don't you come on shore for a run to warm yourself?' said Assipattle. 'Because,' said the man, 'if the Kemperman found me out of the boat, he would half kill me.' 'Wise enough,' says Assipattle; 'you like a cold skin better than a hot. But I must kindle a fire to roast a few limpits, for hunger's like to eat a hole in my stomach.' And with that he began to scrape a hole in the ground, wherein to make a fire. In a minute he cried out, 'My stars! gold! gold! As sure as I am the son of my mother, there's gold in this earth!' When the man in the boat heard this, he jumped on shore, and pushed Assipattle roughly aside. And while the man scraped in the earth, Assipattle seized his pot, loosened the boat-rope, jumped into the boat, and pushed out to sea, while the man roared to, and banned him from the land. As the sun began to peep over the hills, Assipattle hoisted his sail and steered for the head of the Stoorworm. The monster lay before him like an exceedingly big and high mountain, while the eyes of the monster – some say he had but one eye – glowed and flamed like a ward fire. It was a sight that might well have terrified the bravest heart. The monster's length stretched half across the world. His awful tongue was hundreds on hundreds of miles long. And, when in anger, with his tongue he would sweep whole towns, trees, and hills into the sea. His terrible tongue was forked. And the prongs of the fork he used as a pair of tongs, with which to seize his prey. With that fork he would crush the largest ship like an egg-shell. With that fork he would crack the walls of the biggest castle like a nut, and suck every living thing out of the castle into his maw. But Assipattle had no fear.

By this time the king and all his men-folk came to the shore. They saw the boat, and the king knew it to be his boat; whereat he was in great wrath.

Assipattle sailed up to the side of the Stoorworm's head; then, taking down his sail, he lay quietly on his oars, thinking his own thoughts. When the sun struck the Stoorworm's eyes, then he gave a hideous yawn – the first of the seven that he yawned before his awful breakfast. There was a while between each yawn; and you must know it took him a good while to yawn. Now, whenever the monster yawned, a great tide of water rushed into his mouth. Assipattle rowed close to the side of the Stoorworm's mouth; and at the second yawn, the boat was caught on the in-rushing tide, and swept into the monster's mouth. But she did not stay there; for the tide carried her down the monster's black throat, that yawned like a bottomless pit. You may think it was very dark for Assipattle; but no – the roof and sides of the throat being covered with meeracles,[15] that gave a soft, silvery light in the awful creature's throat. On and on, down and down, went Assipattle, for a long length of a way. Take a care of us all! But so might I thrive, as I would not like to go down such a stair! He steered his boat in mid-stream; and as he went down, the water became more shallow, by reason of the many passages that opened on each side of the throat, like the mouths of great caves. Part of the water went through these passages. Now the roof of the throat began to get lower, till the boat's mast stuck its end in the roof, and her keel stuck on the bottom of the throat.

Then Assipattle jumped out; and, pot in hand, waded and ran, and better ran, till he came to the enormous liver of the monster. Then he took his gully, and cut a hole in the liver, and placed the live peat in the hole. And if he did not blow on the burning peat, he did nothing. He blew till he thought his lips would crack. At length the peat began to flame; the flame caught the oil of the liver, and in a minute there was a stately euse.[16] In troth, I think it gave the Stoorworm a hot harskit.[17] Then Assipattle ran back to the boat as fast as his feet could carry him. When the Stoorworm felt the heat of the fire in his inside, he began to spew as if he would have brought up the bottom of his bowels. Then there arose from his huge stomach terrible floods. One of these floods caught the boat, snapped the mast like a trinlie pin, and flung boat and man high and dry on the land.

The king and the folk drew back to a high hill, where they were safe from the floods sent out by the monster, and from his fearful rifts[18] of fire and smoke. The Stoorworm was a terrible sight to see; and every one who saw it could only say, 'What am I born to see!' After the floods of water, there came from the monster's mouth and nose great clouds of smoke black as pitch. It was dismal to see the agonies of the Stoorworm, as the fire grew great within him. He flung out his awful tongue and waved it to and fro. Then, in his agony of pain, he flung up his tongue till its end struck the moon. He gripped one of the moon's horns in the fork of his tongue. Some say he shifted the moon. Now, by good luck, the fork slipped over the end of the horn, otherwise he might have brought down the moon. The tongue fell on the earth with a terrible travellye.[19] So vehement was its fall that it clove the earth, and made a long length of a sea where was once dry land. That is the sea that now divides Denmark from Swedeland and Norawa. They say that at the head of that sea are two great bays,[20] formed by the two prongs of the fork on the Stoorworm's tongue. Then the Stoorworm drew in his long tongue; and his struggles and twisting were a world's terror to behold. He drew himself slowly together in a lump; and, as he did so, the fiery pain made him fling up his head to the clouds; and, anon, it would fall into the sea with a force that shook the world. Take a care of us all! Once, as his head fell, the force of the fall knocked out a number of his teeth, and these teeth became the Orkney Islands. Another time his head rose and fell, when he shed a lot more of his teeth; and these teeth became the Shetland Islands. A third time his head fell from the sky, again throwing out a number of teeth, which became the Faroe Islands. Then the Stoorworm coiled himself up into a great lump; and that lump became Iceland. And then the Stoorworm died. And so may all evil end! Folk say he was a bairn of the Devil. And, troth, he was very like his father, and did his father's will. But, by my certie, he got hard wages for all his work. And so all are served that serve the Devil.

The Stoorworm died; but he still burns under the island. And the fire of that burning makes the burning mountains in Iceland.

And now I must tell you how it fared with Assipattle. The king took him in his arms, and kissed him, and blessed him, and called him his son. The king took off his own mantle and put it on him. And the king took the hand of Gemdelovely and put it in Assipattie's hand. And he girded the great sword Sickersnapper on Assipattle. Assipattle mounted Teetgong, and rode by Gemdelovely's side. And as they all rode in joy for the king's house, Assipattle's sister came running to meet them. She whispered in Gemdelovely's ear, and Gemdelovely told the king what she said. Then the king's face grew dark and door. For she told him the sorcerer had been making love to the queen all the morning. 'I'll go and kill him,' said the king. 'Nay,' said the maid, 'they have both fled, on the two best horses in the stable.' 'They'll ride fast if I don't find them,' said Assipattle. And, with that, he went off like the wind on Teetgong. Assipattle soon came close up with the two evil-doers. And when the sorcerer saw him come so near, he said to the queen, 'It's only some halflin[21] brat; I'll cut off his head in a minute.' So he turned and drew his sword. For he well knew that no common steel could pierce his enchanted body. Then Assipattle drew Sickersnapper; and with one dread thrust he drove the sword through the sorcerer's heart till its point came out at his back. And his blood ran on the ground, black as pitch. The queen was shut up all her days in a high tower.

Assipattle and Gemdelovely were married. And there was a great wedding feast, that lasted nine weeks. The king's Scald made a long rhyme; and the Menyesingers[22] sang a beautiful song. I do not know the words of the song, but this was the owercome[23] –

'The bonniest steen i' a' the land's abeun the king's ha'
   door;
He[24] cam' oot o' a filty hol', whar' he lay lang afore.'

At that wedding all went jolly as a feast in Yule. Assipattle and Gemdelovely were king and queen, and lived in joy and splendour. And, if not dead, they are yet alive.[25]

LEGENDS AND TRADITIONS

Legends and Traditions

THE PECHS*

'Long ago there were people in this country called the Pechs; short wee men they were, wi' red hair, and long arms, and feet sae braid, that when it rained they could turn them up owre their heads, and then they served for umbrellas. The Pechs were great builders; they built a' the auld castles in the kintry; and do ye ken the way they built them? I'll tell ye. They stood all in a row from the quarry to the place where they were building, and ilk ane handed forward the stanes to his neebor, till the hale was biggit. The Pechs were also a great people for ale, which they brewed frae heather; sae, ye ken, it bood[1] to be an extraornar cheap kind of drink; for heather, I'se warrant, was as plenty then as it's now. This art o' theirs was muckle sought after by the other folk that lived in the kintry; but they never would let out the secret, but handed it down frae father to son among themselves, wi' strict injunctions frae ane to another never to let onybody ken about it.

'At last the Pechs had great wars, and mony o' them were killed, and indeed they soon came to be a mere handfu' o' people, and were like to perish aff the face o' the earth. Still

*Chambers, *Popular Rhymes* of *Scotland*. [1]Was bound.

they held fast by their secret of the heather yill, determined that their enemies should never wring it frae them. Weel, it came at last to a great battle between them and the Scots, in which they clean lost the day, and were killed a' to tway, a father and a son. And sae the king o' the Scots had these men brought before him, that he might try to frighten them into telling him the secret. He plainly told them that, if they would not disclose it peaceably, he must torture them till they should confess, and therefore it would be better for them to yield in time. "Weel," says the auld man to the king, "I see it is of no use to resist. But there is ae condition ye maun agree to before ye learn the secret." "And what is that?" said the king. "Will ye promise to fulfil it, if it be na onything against your ain interests?" said the man. "Yes," said the king, "I will and do promise so." Then said the Pech, "You must know that I wish for my son's death, though I dinna like to take his life myself.

> My son ye maun kill,
> Before I will you tell
> How we brew the yill
> Frae the heather bell!"

The king was dootless greatly astonished at sic a request; but, as he had promised, he caused the lad to be immediately put to death. When the auld man saw his son was dead, he started up wi' a great stend,[1] and cried, "Now, do wi' me as you like. My son ye might have forced, for he was but a weak youth; but me you never can force.

> And though you may me kill,
> I will not you tell
> How we brew the yill
> Frae the heather bell!"

[1]Bound.

'The king was now mair astonished than before, but it was at his being sae far outwitted by a mere wild man. Hooever, he saw it was needless to kill the Pech, and that his greatest punishment might now be his being allowed to live. So he was taken away as a prisoner, and he lived for mony a year after that, till he became a very, very auld man, baith bedrid and blind. Maist folk had forgotten there was sic a man in life; but ae night, some young men being in the house where he was, and making great boasts about their feats o' strength, he leaned owre the bed and said he would like to feel ane o' their wrists, that he might compare it wi' the arms of men wha had lived in former times. And they, for sport, held out a thick gaud o' ern[1] to him to feel. He just snappit it in tway wi' his fingers as ye wad do a pipe stapple. "It's a bit gey gristle," he said; "but naething to the shackle-banes o' my days." That was the last o' the Pechs.'

THE WORME OF LINTON*

Crossing the Border into Roxburghshire, we approach the haunts of the Worme of Linton, and very romantic they are. There is the mountain stream of the Kale, bursting in brightness from the Cheviot Hills, and hurrying into the plain below, where it pauses, ere it wends its way to join the Teviot; there is the low, irregular mound, marking where stood the Tower of Linton, the stronghold of the Somervilles; there is the old village church, standing on its remarkable knoll of sand; there are the stately woods of

[1]Rod of iron.
*William Henderson, *Notes on the Folk-Lore of the Northern Counties of England and the Borders.*

Clifton, and, above all, the lofty heights of Cheviot
crowning the distance.

Such is the fair scene which tradition avers was once laid
waste by a fierce and voracious monster. His den, still
named the 'Worm's Hole', lay in a hollow to the east of the
Hill of Linton; and small need had he to leave it, for from
this retreat he could with his sweeping and venomous
breath draw the neighbouring flocks and herds within
reach of his fangs. Still he did occasionally emerge and coil
himself round an eminence of some height, at no great
distance, still bearing the name of Wormington or
Wormiston. Liberal guerdons were offered to any
champion who would rid the country of such a scourge, but
in vain – such was the dread inspired by the monster's
poisonous breath. Not only were the neighbouring villagers
beside themselves with terror, but the inhabitants of
Jedburgh, full ten miles off, were struck with such a panic
that they were ready to desert their town.

At last, however, the Laird of Lariston, a man of reckless
bravery, came forward to the rescue of this distressed
district; and, as the Linton cottagers testify to this day,
having once failed in an attack with ordinary weapons, he
resorted to the expedient of thrusting down the worm's
throat a peat dipped in scalding pitch and fixed on his
lance. The device proved perfectly successful. The aromatic
quality of the burning pitch, while it suffocated and choked
the monster, preserved the champion from the effects of its
poison-laden breath. While dying, the worm is said to have
contracted its folds with such violent muscular energy that
the sides of Wormington Hill are still marked with their
spiral impressions. In requital of his service, the Laird of
Lariston received the gift of extensive lands in the neighbourhood.

THE LEGEND OF LINTON CHURCH*

There is another legend connected with Linton of exceeding interest. It is sometimes interwoven with that of the Worm, but I am informed that in its more correct form it stands alone. The church is built on a little knoll of fine compact sand, without any admixture of stone, or even pebbles, and widely differing from the soil of the neighbouring heights. The sand has nowhere hardened into stone, yet the particles are so coherent, that the sides of newly-opened graves appear smooth as a wall, and this to the depth of fifteen feet. This singular phenomenon is thus accounted for on the spot:

Many ages ago a young man killed a priest in this place; and was condemned to suffer death for murder and sacrilege. His doom seemed inevitable, but powerful intercession was made for him, especially by his two sisters, who were fondly attached to their brother. At last his life was granted him, on condition that the sisters should sift as much sand as would form a mound on which to build a church. The maidens joyfully undertook the task, and their patience did not fail. They completed it, and the church was built, though it is added that one of the sisters died immediately after her brother's liberation, either from the effects of past fatigue or overpowering joy. Such is the version of the legend, deemed the correct one at Linton. The villagers point to the sandy knoll in confirmation of its truth, and show a hollow place, a short distance to the westward, as that from which the sand was taken.

*William Henderson, *Notes on the Folk-Lore of the Northern Counties of England and the Borders.*

THOMAS THE RHYMER*

Few personages are so renowned in tradition as Thomas of Ercildoune, known by the appellation of The Rhymer. Uniting, or supposing to unite, in his person, the powers of poetical composition and of vaticination, his memory, even after the lapse of five hundred years, is regarded with veneration by his countrymen. To give anything like a certain history of this remarkable man would be indeed difficult but the curious may derive some satisfaction from the particulars here brought together

It is agreed on all hands, that the residence, and probably the birthplace, of this ancient bard was Ercildoune, a village situated upon the Leader, two miles above its junction with the Tweed. The ruins of an ancient tower are still pointed out as the Rhymer's castle. The uniform tradition bears, that his surname was Lermont, or Learmont; and that the appellation of The Rhymer was conferred on him in consequence of his poetical compositions. There remains, nevertheless, some doubt upon the subject.

We are better able to ascertain the period at which Thomas of Ercildoune lived, being the latter end of the thirteenth century.

It cannot be doubted that Thomas was a remarkable and important person in his own time, since, very shortly after his death, we find him celebrated as a prophet and as a poet. Whether he himself made any pretensions to the first of these characters, or whether it was gratuitously conferred upon him by the credulity of posterity, it seems difficult to decide.

Whatever doubts, however, the learned might have as to the source of the Rhymer's prophetic skill, the vulgar had

Sir Walter Scott, *Minstrelsy of the Scottish Border.*

no hesitation to ascribe the whole to the intercourse between the bard and the Queen of Faery. The popular tale bears that Thomas was carried off, at an early age, to the Fairy Land, where he acquired all the knowledge which made him afterwards so famous. After seven years' residence he was permitted to return to the earth, to enlighten and astonish his countrymen by his prophetic powers; still, however, remaining bound to return to his royal mistress, when she should intimate her pleasure. Accordingly, while Thomas was making merry with his friends in the Tower of Ercildoune, a person came running in, and told, with marks of fear and astonishment, that a hart and hind had left the neighbouring forest, and were, composedly and slowly, parading the street of the village. The prophet instantly arose, left his habitation, and followed the wonderful animals to the forest, whence he was never seen to return. According to the popular belief, he still 'drees his weird' in Fairy Land, and is one day expected to revisit earth. In the meanwhile, his memory is held in the most profound respect. The Eildon Tree, from beneath the shade of which he delivered his prophecies, now no longer exists; but the spot is marked by a large stone, called Eildon Tree Stone. A neighbouring rivulet takes the name of the Bogle Burn (Goblin Brook) from the Rhymer's supernatural visitants.

MICHAEL SCOTT*

In the early part of Michael Scott's life he was in the habit of emigrating annually to the Scottish metropolis, for the purpose of being employed in his capacity of mason. One

*W. Grant Stewart, *Popular Superstitions of the Highlanders*.

time as he and two companions were journeying to the place of their destination for a similar object, they had occasion to pass over a high hill, the name of which is not mentioned, but which is supposed to have been one of the Grampians, and being fatigued with climbing, they sat down to rest themselves. They had no sooner done so than they were warned to take to their heels by the hissing of a large serpent, which they observed revolving itself towards them with great velocity. Terrified at the sight, Michael's two companions fled, while he, on the contrary, resolved to encounter the reptile. The appalling monster approached Michael Scott with distended mouth and forked tongue; and, throwing itself into a coil at his feet, was raising its head to inflict a mortal sting, when Michael, with one stroke of his stick, severed its body into three pieces. Having rejoined his affrighted comrades, they resumed their journey; and on arriving at the next public-house, it being late, and the travellers being weary, they took up their quarters at it for the night. In the course of the night's conversation, reference was naturally made to Michael's recent exploit with the serpent, when the landlady of the house, who was remarkable for her 'arts', happened to be present. Her curiosity appeared much excited by the conversation; and, after making some inquiries regarding the colour of the serpent, which she was told was white, she offered any of them that would procure her the middle piece such a tempting reward, as induced one of the party instantly to go for it. The distance was not very great; and on reaching the spot, he found the middle and tail piece in the place where Michael left them, but the head piece was gone.

The landlady on receiving the piece, which still vibrated with life, seemed highly gratified at her acquisition; and,

over and above the promised reward, regaled her lodgers
very plentifully with the choicest dainties in her house.
Fired with curiosity to know the purpose for which the
serpent was intended, the wily Michael Scott was immediately seized with a severe fit of indisposition, which caused
him to prefer the request that he might be allowed to sleep
beside the fire, the warmth of which, he affirmed, was in
the highest degree beneficial to him.

Never suspecting Michael Scott's hypocrisy, and
naturally supposing that a person so severely indisposed
would feel very little curiosity about the contents of any
cooking utensils which might lie around the fire, the landlady allowed his request. As soon as the other inmates of
the house were retired to bed, the landlady resorted to her
darling occupation; and, in his feigned state of indisposition, Michael had a favourable opportunity of watching
most scrupulously all her actions through the keyhole of a
door leading to the next apartment where she was. He
could see the rites and ceremonies with which the serpent
was put into the oven, along with many mysterious
ingredients. After which the unsuspicious landlady placed
the dish by the fireside, where lay the distressed traveller, to
stove till the morning.

Once or twice in the course of the night the 'wife of the
change-house', under the pretence of inquiring for her sick
lodger, and administering to him some renovating cordials,
the beneficial effects of which he gratefully acknowledged,
took occasion to dip her finger in her saucepan, upon
which the cock, perched on his roost, crowed aloud. All
Michael's sickness could not prevent him considering very
inquisitively the landlady's cantrips,[1] and particularly the
influence of the sauce upon the crowing of the cock. Nor

[1]Spells.

could he dissipate some inward desires he felt to follow her example. At the same time, he suspected that Satan had a hand in the pie, yet he thought he would like very much to be at the bottom of the concern; and thus his reason and his curiosity clashed against each other for the space of several hours. At length passion, as is too often the case, became the conqueror. Michael, too, dipped his finger in the sauce, and applied it to the tip of his tongue, and immediately the cock perched on the *spardan* announced the circumstance in a mournful clarion. Instantly his mind received a new light to which he was formerly a stranger, and the astonished dupe of a landlady now found it her interest to admit her sagacious lodger into a knowledge of the remainder of her secrets.

Endowed with the knowledge of 'good and evil', Michael left his lodgings in the morning with the philosopher's stone in his pocket. By daily perfecting his supernatural attainments, by new series of discoveries, he became more than a match for Satan himself. Having seduced some thousands of Satan's best workmen into his employment, he trained them up so successfully to the architective business, and inspired them with such industrious habits, that he was more than sufficient for all the architectural work of the empire. To establish this assertion, we need only refer to some remains of his workmanship still existing north of the Grampians, some of them, stupendous bridges built by him in one short night, with no other visible agents than two or three workmen.

On one occasion work was getting scarce, as might have been naturally expected, and his workmen, as they were wont, flocked to his doors, perpetually exclaiming, 'Work! work! work!' Continually annoyed by their incessant entreaties, he called out to them in derision to go and make a dry road from Fortrose to Arderseir, over the Moray Firth. Immediately their cry ceased, and as Scott supposed it wholly impossible for them to execute his order, he retired to rest, laughing most heartily at the chimerical sort of employment he had given to his industrious workmen. Early in the morning, however, he got up and took a walk at the break of day down to the shore to divert himself at the fruitless labours of his zealous workmen. But on reaching the spot, what was his astonishment to find the formidable piece of work allotted to them only a few hours before already nearly finished. Seeing the great damage the commercial class of the community would sustain from the operation, he ordered the workmen to demolish the most part of their work; leaving, however, the point of Fortrose to show the traveller to this day the wonderful exploit of Michael Scott's fairies.

On being thus again thrown out of employment, their former clamour was resumed, nor could Michael Scott, with all his sagacity, devise a plan to keep them in innocent employment. He at length discovered one. 'Go,' says he, 'and manufacture me ropes that will carry me to the back of the moon, of these materials – *miller's-sudds* and sea-sand.' Michael Scott here obtained rest from his active operators; for, when other work failed them, he always despatched them to their rope manufactory. But though these agents could never make proper ropes of those materials, their efforts to that effect are far from being contemptible, for some of their ropes are seen by the sea-side to this day.

In consequence of a violent quarrel which Michael Scott once had with a person whom he conceived to have caused him some injury, he resolved, as the highest punishment he could inflict upon him, to send his adversary to that evil place designed only for Satan and his black companions. He accordingly, by means of his supernatural machinations, sent the poor unfortunate man thither; and had he been sent by any other means than those of Michael Scott, he would no doubt have met with a warm reception. Out of pure spite to Michael, however, when Satan learned who was his billet-master, he would no more receive him than he would receive the Wife of Beth; and instead of treating the unfortunate man with the harshness characteristic of him, he showed him considerable civilities. Introducing him to his 'Ben Taigh', he directed her to show the stranger any curiosities he might wish to see, hinting very significantly that he had provided some accommodation for their mutual friend, Michael Scott, the sight of which might afford him some gratification. The polite housekeeper accordingly conducted the stranger through the principal apartments in the house, where he saw fearful sights. But the bed of Michael Scott! – his greatest enemy could not but feel satiated with revenge at the sight of it. It was a place too horrid to be described, filled promiscuously with all the awful brutes imaginable. Toads and lions, lizards and leeches, and, amongst the rest, not the least conspicuous, a large serpent gaping for Michael Scott, with its mouth wide open. This last sight having satisfied the stranger's curiosity, he was led to the outer gate, and came away. He reached his friends, and, among other pieces of news touching his travels, he was not backward in relating the entertainment that awaited his friend Michael Scott, as soon as he would 'stretch his foot' for the other world. But Michael did not at all appear disconcerted at his friend's intelligence. He affirmed that he would disappoint all his enemies in their expectations – in proof of which he gave the following signs: 'When I am just dead,' says he, 'open my breast and extract my heart. Carry it to some place where the public may see the result. You will then transfix it upon a long pole, and if Satan will have my soul, he will come in the likeness of a black raven and carry it off; and if my soul will be saved it will be carried off by a white dove.'

His friends faithfully obeyed his instructions. Having exhibited his heart in the manner directed, a large black raven was observed to come from the east with great fleetness, while a white dove came from the west with equal velocity. The raven made a furious dash at the heart, missing which, it was unable to curb its force, till it was considerably past it; and the dove, reaching the spot at the same time, carried off the heart amidst the rejoicing and ejaculations of the spectators.

THE GHOST THAT DANCED AT JETHART*

This legend carries us back to the time of Alexander III, of revered memory – to a time when Scotland was enjoying – what was not often her wont – such an amount of rest from turmoil, that she could participate a little in harmless ostentation and brilliant pageantry. Such brilliant pageantry occurred in 1285 at Jedburgh, which Alexander had fixed upon, from the celebrity of its abbey and the attractiveness of its surrounding scenery, as a fitting place wherein to celebrate his marriage with Yolande, daughter of the Count de Dreux. Jedburgh was thus in high holiday; but at the banquet in the evening – more splendid, we are told, than anything of the kind previously seen in Scotland – held, it is said, in the great hall of the abbey, and at the very

*The Border Counties' Magazine.

moment when the hilarity of the brilliant assemblage was at its highest – when the dance had grown fast and furious, and all went merry as a marriage bell – there took place a remarkable, ghostly incident. One of the exhibitions of the evening consisted of a kind of military dance or procession. While this dance was performing, and while the mirth was unbounded, an unwelcome visitor appeared at the festive board, whose presence put a sudden end to the hilarities of the evening. At the close of the procession of maskers, a spectre glided into the room and mixed in the dance, at sight of which the music ceased in an instant, and the maskers fled in affright. In the midst of the turmoil, the spectre suddenly disappeared. The incident of the skeleton dancer was too remarkable not to become associated in the public mind with national disaster. Accordingly an old poet connects with the apparition the fact that:

> 'The king soon after, falling from his steed,
> Unhappily died, – after whose death, ensuing
> Woe to the land, sedition, wreck, and ruin.'

THE TALE OF SIR JAMES RAMSAY OF BAMFF*

'Weel, ye see, I dinna mind the beginning o' the story. But the Sir James Ramsay o' Bamff of that time was said to be ane o' the conspirators, and his lands were forfaulted, and himsel' banished the country, and a price set upon his head if he came back.

'He gaed to France or Spain, I'm no sure which, and was very ill off. Ae day that he was walking in a wood, he met

*Chambers, *Popular Rhymes*.

an oldish man wi' a lang beard, weel dressed and respectable looking. This man lookit hard at Sir James and then said to him that he lookit ill and distressed like; that he himsel' was a doctor, and if Sir James would tell his complaints, maybe he might be able to do him good.

'Syne Sir James said he was not ill but for want o' food, and that all the medicine he needed was some way to earn his living as a gentleman. The auld doctor said till him he would take him as an apprentice if he liked; that he should live in his house and at his table, and learn his profession. So Sir James went hame wi' him, and was very kindly tret. After he had been wi' him a while, his master said till him ae day that he kend how to make the best and most wonderful medicine in the world – a medicine that would make baith their fortunes, and a' that belanged to them; but that it was a difficult business to get the materials that the medicine was made of – that they could only be gotten frae the river ——, that ran through the county of ——, in Scotland, and at a particular part of the river, which he described; and that it would need to be some canny person, that kend that pairt o' the country weel, to gang wi' ony chance o' success. Sir James said naebody kend that pairt o' the country better than himsel', for it was on his ain estate o' Bamff, and that he was very willing to run the risk o' going hame for his master's sake, that had been sae kind to him, and for the sake o' seeing his ain place again.

'Then the doctor gied him strict directions what he was to do, and how he was to make sure o' getting the beast that he was to make the medicine o'. He was to gang to a pairt o' the river where there was a deep pool o' water, and he was to hide himsel' behind some big trees that came down to the water-side for the three nights that the moon was at the full. He would see a white serpent come out o' the water, and go up to a big stane, and creep under it. He maun watch till it came out again, and catch it on its way back to the water, and kill it, and bring it awa' wi' him.

'Weel, Sir James did a' that he was bidden. He put on a disguise, and gaed back to Scotland and to Bamff, and got there without onybody kenning him. He hid himsel' behind the trees at the water-side, and watched night after night. He saw the white serpent come out the first twa nights, and creep under the stane; but it aye got back to the water afore he could catch it; but the third night he did catch it, and killed it, and brought it awa' wi' him to Spain to his master. His master was very glad to get it, but he wasna sae kind after to Sir James as he used to be. He told him, now that they had got the serpent, the next thing to do was to cook it, and he maun do that too. He was to go down to a vault, and there stew the serpent till it was turned into oil. If onybody saw him at the wark, or if he tasted food till it was done, the charm would be spoiled; and if by ony chance he was to taste the medicine, it would kill him at ance, unless he had the proper remedy. Sae Sir James gaed down to the vault, and prepared the medicine just as he had been ordered; but when he was pouring it out o' the pan into the box where it was to be keepit, he let some drops fa' on his fingers that brunt them; and in the pain and hurry he forgot his master's orders, and put his fingers into his mouth to suck out the pain. He did not die, but he fand that his een were opened, and that he could see through everything. And when his master came down at the appointed time to speer if the medicine was ready, he fand he could see into his master's inside, and could tell a' that was going on there. But he keepit his ain secret, and never let on to his master what had happened; and it was very lucky, for he soon found out that his master was a bad man, and would have killed him if he had kend that he had got the secret o' the medicine. He had only been kind to him because he kend that Sir James was the best man to catch the serpent. However, Sir James learnt to be a skilfu' doctor under him; and at last he managed to get awa' frae him, and syne he travelled over the warld as a doctor, doing mony wonders, because he could clearly see what was wrang in folk's insides. But he wearied sair to get back to Scotland, and he thought that naebody would ken him as a doctor. Sae he ventured to gae back; and when he arrived, he fand that the king was very ill, and no man could find out what was the matter wi' him. He had tried a' the doctors in Scotland, and a' that came to him frae far and near, but he was nane the better; and at last he published a proclamation, that he would gie the princess, his daughter, in marriage to ony man that would cure him. Sae Sir James gaed to the court, and askit leave to try his skill. As soon as he came into the king's presence, and looked at him, he saw there was a ball o' hair in his inside, and that no medicine could touch it. But he said if the king would trust to him, he would cure him; and the king having consented, he put him sae fast asleep, that he cuttit the ball o' hair out of his inside without his ever wakening. When he did waken, he was free from illness, only weak a little frae the loss o' blood; and he was sae pleased wi' his doctor, that Sir James kneeled down and tell't him wha he was. And the king pardoned him, and gied him back a' his lands, and gied him the princess, his daughter, in marriage.'

THE LEE PENNY*

The following adventure is said to have befallen Sir Simon Lockhart, whilst fighting against the Saracens in the Holy Land. He made prisoner in battle an Emir of wealth and note. The aged mother of his captive came to the Christian camp to redeem her son from his captivity. Lockhart fixed the price at which his prisoner should ransom himself; and the lady, pulling out a large embroidered purse, proceeded to tell down the amount. In this operation, a pebble inserted in a coin, some say of the lower empire, fell out of the purse, and the Saracen matron testified so much haste to recover it as to give the Scottish knight a high idea of its value. 'I will not consent,' he said, 'to grant your son's liberty unless the amulet be added to the ransom.' The lady not only consented to this, but explained to Sir Simon the mode in which the talisman was to be used. The water in which it was dipped operated either as a styptic, or as a febrifuge, and the amulet besides possessed several other properties as a medical talisman.

Sir Simon Lockhart, after much experience of the wonders which it wrought, brought it to his own country, and left it to his heirs, by whom, and by Clydeside in general, it was, and is still, distinguished by the name of the Lee Penny, from the name of his native seat of Lee.

The virtues were brought into operation by dropping the stone into water given to the diseased to drink, washing at the same time the part affected. No words were used in dipping the stone, or money permitted to be taken by the servants of Lee. People came from all parts of Scotland, and many places in England, to carry away water to give to their cattle.

*Mr William Andrews, in the *Border Counties' Magazine*.

The amulet is a stone of a deep red colour and triangular shape – each side being about half an inch in length – set in a piece of silver coin.

BOASTING PUNISHED*

A highlander's glory and felicity consisted in the extent of his fold, and the number of his family.

He could never have too many children, or too many cows; however great the difficulty might be of rearing the first to maturity, or providing winter fodder for the last. But to parade either one's cows, or one's children, in any unnecessary display, or for a stranger to make any remark on the abundance of them, is by no means safe.

Of this superstition numberless instances might be given. Of these, the most signalised which I recollect derives interest from the royal and beautiful personage concerned in it; it is said to have happened when Queen Mary made that memorable excursion to the North, which proved so fatal to the Gordons.

She stayed for some days at Inverness, in the castle (so well known as the scene of King Duncan's murder), and received there the homage of all the neighbouring gentry and nobility.

There lived at that time in Ross-shire a wealthy and powerful family of the name of Monro, whose title I do not remember.

The laird had been attending his sovereign with all due loyalty on her expedition. The lady had twelve sons, and twelve daughters, many of whom were married, or otherwise detached from the family.

*Mrs Grant, of Laggan, *Superstitions of the Highlanders*.

She was at much pains, however, in collecting them, wherever they were dispersed, to adorn her train, in the presence of royalty.

The sons were all dressed in 'Lincoln green', the wonted costume of knights and hunters, and led the procession in gallant array, mounted upon sable steeds. Next, their mother, decked no doubt in her best array, followed, attended by her daughters, attired in white, and mounted on horses of the same colour. This goodly train was ushered into the royal presence, after being duly announced. The matron, dropping on one knee, made obeisance, and told her sovereign she had here brought twelve squires and twelve damsels, ready to devote themselves to her service. The queen started from her seat, overwhelmed with astonishment and admiration, and cried, 'Madam, ye sud tak this chair, ye best deserve it.' After this exclamation, the ceremonial was properly adjusted, and the family returned home, enchanted with the grace and loveliness of their accomplished sovereign. It was, however, remarked, that from that day they were never again seen together, and that this imprudent mother was the sad survivor of the far greater number of the children thus rashly exhibited.

THE CRAIG LIATH MHOR*

At the foot of Glen Errochdie, on the road between Struan and Rannoch, stand the ruins of the ancient farmhouse of Blairfettie. The present building is comparatively a modern structure, having been built somewhere about the middle of the present century; but the one I refer to is situated across

*Mr John Kennedy's MS.

the river immediately opposite the present one. It is now a complete ruin, and, in fact, its site is almost obliterated. At the foot of a birch plantation, and in close proximity to the river Errochdie, it formerly commanded an extensive view of the glen. Towards the latter end of the seventeenth century, it was the property of a certain Laird of Muirlaggan, Rannoch, who resided there along with his eleven sons, all but one of whom were manly and stalwart Highlanders.

Their mother having died when giving birth to the youngest – a fair-haired, sickly-looking child – the sons resolved to remain at home to support and comfort their venerable father in his declining years.

Being muscular and powerful fellows, their sole delight was in fishing and hunting, and exerting and testing their strength at feats of valour and skill. Their aged father they honoured with unbounded respect, always consulting him before engaging in any contemplated hunting or deer-stalking expedition.

The youngest brother, who was at the period of my tale only about sixteen years of age, would never consent to join his bigger brothers in their games, as his disposition was perfectly opposite to theirs, he preferring to roam amongst the woods and down the river's side in quest of blaeberries and wild flowers.

He was his father's favourite, which, together with his girlish manners, and his utter distaste for manly sports, made him disliked by his brethren.

One morning, towards the fall of the year, the brothers decided on going on a deer-stalking expedition. The place chosen for the chase was the Hill of Tulloch, now part of the Auchlecks estate. Accompanied by their youngest brother, whom they had with some difficulty induced to join them, and taking with them a few couples of stag-hounds, which they held in leashes, they started on their journey, striding along gaily and enlivening the way with merry banter and chat, whilst teasing and tormenting their youngest brother on his unsportsmanlike appearance.

Attaining the summit of the hill, they at once engaged in the hunt, which was continued up to midday, when they decided to rest and partake of their oatmeal bannocks and usquebaugh. The spot where they rested is called the 'Craig Liath Mhor', which, literally translated, means the 'Big Grey Crag'.

Having partaken of their meal, they engaged in conversation, to while the time away before again resuming the chase.

During the course of their talk, the deer-hounds suddenly commenced to quarrel and fight, and would upon no account be separated, although various measures were resorted to to quell and subdue them. All attempts at pacification proving futile, the company in the last resort resolved to let the outrageous animals fight it out, and thereupon sat down to witness the result. Wagers were freely engaged in, and out of one of these wagers there arose a quarrel between two of the brothers. Like the dogs, they were determined to fight it out, and agreed to settle the dispute at the point of the dirk.

The rest of the brothers, unwilling that any such affair should disgrace their family, strove their utmost to separate the two combatants; but, instead of quelling the dispute, they only succeeded in adding fuel to the fire.

Without further ado lots were cast, and a general and equal-sided fight then began.

Fierce and bloody was the fray, and melancholy the result; for not a single man of the brothers remained alive at the end of it, except the youngest, who had taken no active part in the combat.

He returned to his father with the sad and terrible tidings of what had occurred; upon hearing which the wretched man was heart-broken, and within a few days succumbed to his grief. What became of the survivor I cannot tell, as all traces of him seem to have been lost.

On the summit of the 'Craig Liath Mhor' may be seen to this day ten cairns, which mark the last resting-place of the brothers. A few stones roughly piled one above the other are all that mark the spot where the fatal struggle took place.

FIDDLER'S WELL*

. . . The path rises by a kind of natural stair to the top of the precipices, and continues to ascend till it reaches a spring of limpid water, which comes gushing out of the side of a bank covered with moss and daisies, and which for more than a century has been known to the townspeople by the name of Fiddler's Well. Its waters are said to be medicinal, and there is a pretty tradition still extant of the circumstance through which their virtues were first discovered, and to which the spring owes its name.

Two young men of Cromarty, who were much attached to each other, were seized at nearly the same time by consumption. In one the progress of the disease was rapid – he died two short months after he was attacked by it; while the other, though wasted almost to a shadow, had yet strength enough left to follow the corpse of his companion to the grave. The name of the survivor was Fiddler – a name

*Hugh Miller, *Scenes and Legends of the North of Scotland*.

still common among the seafaring men of the town. On the evening of the interment he felt oppressed and unhappy; his imagination was haunted by a thousand feverish shapes of open graves with bones mouldering round their edges, and of coffins with the lids displaced; and after he had fallen asleep, the images, which were still the same, became more ghastly and horrible. Towards morning, however, they had all vanished; and he dreamed that he was walking alone by the sea-shore in a clear and beautiful day of summer. Suddenly, as he thought, some person stepped up behind, and whispered in his ear, in the voice of his deceased companion, 'Go on, Willie; I shall meet you at *Stormy*.' There is a rock in the neighbourhood of Fiddler's Well, so called, from the violence with which the sea beats against it when the wind blows strongly from the east. On hearing the voice he turned round, and, seeing no one, he went on, as he thought, to the place named, in the hope of meeting his friend, and sat down on a bank to wait his coming; but he waited long – lonely and dejected; and then remembering that he for whom he waited was dead, he burst into tears. At this moment a large field-bee came humming from the west, and began to fly round his head. He raised his hand to brush it away; it widened its circle, and then came humming into his ear as before. He raised his hand a second time, but the bee would not be scared off; it hummed ceaselessly round and round him, until at length its murmurings seemed to be fashioned into words, articulated in the voice of his deceased companion. 'Dig, Willie, and drink!' it said; 'Dig, Willie, and drink!' He accordingly set himself to dig, and no sooner had he torn a sod out of the bank than a spring of clear water gushed from the hollow; and the bee, taking a wider circle, and humming in a voice of triumph that seemed to emulate the sound of a distant trumpet, flew away. He looked after it, but as he looked the images of his dream began to mingle with those of the waking world; the scenery of the hill seemed obscured by a dark cloud, in the centre of which there glimmered a faint light; the rocks, the sea, the long declivity faded into the cloud; and turning round he saw only a dark apartment, and the faint beams of morning shining in at a window. He rose, and, after digging the well, drank of the water and recovered. And its virtues are still celebrated; for though the water be only simple water, it must be drunk in the morning, and as it gushes from the bank; and with pure air, exercise, and early rising for its auxiliaries, it continues to work cures.

FAIRY TALES

Fairy Tales

THE FAIRIES OF SCOTLAND

The Fairies of Scotland are represented as a diminutive race of beings, of a mixed, or rather dubious nature, capricious in their dispositions, and mischievous in their resentment. They inhabit the interior of green hills, chiefly those of a conical form, in Gaelic termed Sighan, on which they lead their dances by moonlight; impressing upon the surface the marks of circles, which sometimes appear yellow and blasted, sometimes of a deep green hue; and within which it is dangerous to sleep, or to be found after sunset. The removal of those large portions of turf, which thunderbolts sometimes scoop out of the ground with singular regularity, is also ascribed to their agency. Cattle, which are suddenly seized with the cramp, or some similar disorder, are said to be elf-shot; and the approved cure is, to chafe the parts affected with a blue bonnet, which, it may be readily believed, often restores the circulation. The triangular flints, frequently found in Scotland, with which the ancient inhabitants probably barbed their shafts, are supposed to be the weapons of Fairy resentment, and are termed elf arrow-heads. The rude brazen battle-axes of the ancients,

*Sir Walter Scott, Minstrelsy of the Scottish Border.

commonly called celts, are also ascribed to their manufacture. But, like the Gothic duergar, their skill is not confined to the fabrication of arms; for they are heard sedulously hammering in linns, precipices, and rocky or cavernous situations, where, like the dwarfs of the mines, mentioned by Georg. Agricola, they busy themselves in imitating the actions and the various employments of men. The Brook of Beaumont, for example, which passes, in its course, by numerous linns and caverns, is notorious for being haunted by the Fairies; and the perforated and rounded stones which are formed by trituration in its channel, are termed, by the vulgar, fairy cups and dishes.

It is sometimes accounted unlucky to pass such places, without performing some ceremony to avert the displeasure of the elves. There is, upon the top of Minchmuir, a mountain in Peeblesshire, a spring called the Cheese Well, because, anciently, those who passed that way were wont to throw into it a piece of cheese, as an offering to the Fairies, to whom it was consecrated.

The usual dress of the Fairies is green; though on the moors they have been sometimes observed in heath-brown, or in weeds dyed with the stoneraw, or lichen. They often ride in invisible procession, when their presence is discovered by the shrill ringing of their bridles. On these occasions they sometimes borrow mortal steeds; and when such are found at morning, panting and fatigued in their stalls, with their manes and tails dishevelled and entangled, the grooms, I presume, often find this a convenient excuse for their situation; as the common belief of the elves quaffing the choicest liquors in the cellars of the rich might occasionally cloak the delinquencies of an unfaithful butler.

THE FAIRY AND THE MILLER'S WIFE*

One day as a mother was sitting rocking her baby to sleep, she was surprised, on looking up, to see a lady of elegant and courtly demeanour, so unlike any one she had ever seen in that part of the country, standing in the middle of the room. She had not heard any one enter, therefore you may judge it was with no little surprise, not unmingled with curiosity, that she rose to welcome her strange visitor. She handed her a chair, but she very politely declined to be seated. She was very magnificently attired; her dress was of the richest green, embroidered round with spangles of gold, and on her head was a small coronet of pearls. The woman was still more surprised at her strange request. She asked, in a rich musical voice, if she would oblige her with a basin of oatmeal. A basin full to overflowing was immediately handed to her, for the woman's husband, being both a farmer and miller, had plenty of meal at command. The lady promised to return it, and named the day she would do so. One of the children put out her hand to get hold of the grand lady's spangles, but told her mother afterwards that she felt nothing. The mother was afraid the child would lose the use of her hands, but no such calamity ensued. It would have been very ungrateful in her fairy majesty if she had struck the child powerless for touching her dress, if indeed such power were hers. But to return to our story. The very day mentioned the oatmeal was returned, not by the same lady, but by a curious little figure with a yelping voice; she was likewise dressed in green. After handing the meal, she yelped out, 'Braw meal; it's the top pickle of the sin corn.' It was excellent; and what was very strange, all the family were advised to partake of it but one servant lad,

*Campbell, *Tales of the West Higlands*.

who spurned the fairy's meal; and he dying shortly after, the miller and his wife firmly believed it was because he refused to eat of the meal. They also firmly believed their first visitor was no less a personage than the Queen of the Fairies, who, having dismissed her court, had not one maid of honour in waiting to obey her commands. A few nights after this strange visit, as the miller was going to bed, a gentle tap was heard at the door, and on its being opened by him, with a light in his hand, there stood a little figure dressed in green, who, in a shrill voice, but very polite manner, requested him to let on the water and set the mill in order, for she was going to grind some corn. The miller did not dare to refuse, so did as she desired him. She told him to go to bed again, and he would find all as he had left it. He found everything in the morning as she said he would. So much for the honesty of fairies.

SIR GODFREY MACCULLOCH*

The Scottish Fairies, in like manner, sometimes reside in subterranean abodes, in the vicinity of human habitations, or, according to the popular phrase, under the 'door-stane', or threshold; in which situation they sometimes establish an intercourse with men, by borrowing and lending, and other kindly offices. In this capacity they are termed 'the good neighbours', from supplying privately the wants of their friends, and assisting them in all their trans-actions, while their favours are concealed. Of this the tradi-tionary story of Sir Godfrey Macculloch forms a curious example.

As this Gallovidian gentleman was taking the air on

Sir Walter Scott, *Ministrely of the Scottish Border*.

horseback, near his own house, he was suddenly accosted by a little old man arrayed in green, and mounted upon a white palfrey. After mutual salutation, the old man gave Sir Godfrey to understand that he resided under his habitation, and that he had great reason to complain of the direction of a drain, or common sewer, which emptied itself directly into his chamber of daïs.[1] Sir Godfrey Macculloch was a good deal startled at this extraordinary complaint; but, guessing the nature of the being he had to deal with, he assured the old man, with great courtesy, that the direction of the drain should be altered; and caused it to be done accordingly. Many years afterwards Sir Godfrey had the misfortune to kill, in a fray, a gentleman of the neighbourhood. He was apprehended, tried, and condemned. The scaffold upon which his head was to be struck off was erected on the Castle Hill of Edinburgh; but hardly had he reached the fatal spot when the old man, upon his white palfrey, pressed through the crowd with the rapidity of lightning. Sir Godfrey, at his command, sprung on behind him; the 'good neighbour' spurred his horse down the steep bank, and neither he nor the criminal was ever again seen.

THE LAIRD O' CO'*

In the days of yore, the proprietors of Colzean, in Ayrshire, were known in that country by the title of *Lairds o' Co'*, a name bestowed on Colzean from some co's (or coves) in the rock underneath the castle.

One morning, a very little boy, carrying a small wooden can, addressed the laird near the castle gate, begging for a

[1] Or, best room.
*Chambers, *Popular Rhymes of Scotland*.

little ale for his mother, who was sick: the laird directed him to go to the butler and get his can filled; so away he went as ordered. The butler had a barrel of ale on tap, but about half full, out of which he proceeded to fill the boy's can; but, to his extreme surprise, he emptied the cask, and still the little can was not nearly full. The butler was unwilling to broach another barrel; but the little fellow insisted on the fulfilment of the laird's order, and a reference was made to him by the butler, who stated the miraculously large capacity of the tiny can, and received instant orders to fill it if all the ale in the cellar would suffice. Obedient to this command, he broached another cask, but had scarcely drawn a drop, when the can was full, and the dwarf departed with expressions of gratitude.

Some years afterwards, the laird, being at the wars in Flanders, was taken prisoner, and for some reason or other (probably as a spy) condemned to die a felon's death. The night prior to the day appointed for his execution, being confined in a dungeon strongly barricaded, the doors suddenly flew open, and the dwarf reappeared, saying –

> 'Laird o' Co',
> Rise an' go' –

a summons too welcome to require repetition.

On emerging from prison, the boy caused him to mount on his shoulders, and in a short time set him down at his own gate, on the very spot where they had first met, saying –

> 'Ae guid turn deserves anither –
> Tak ye that for bein' sae kind to my auld mither,'

and vanished.

HABITROT*

In the old days, when spinning was the constant employment of women, the spinning-wheel had its presiding genius or fairy. Her Border name was Habitrot, and Mr Wilkie tells the following legend about her:

A Selkirkshire matron had one fair daughter, who loved play better than work, wandering in the meadows and lanes better than the spinning-wheel and distaff. The mother was heartily vexed at this taste, for in those days no lassie had any chance of a good husband unless she was an industrious spinster. So she cajoled, threatened, even beat her daughter, but all to no purpose; the girl remained what her mother called her, 'an idle cuttie'.

At last, one spring morning, the gudewife gave her seven heads of lint, saying she would take no excuse; they must be returned in three days spun into yarn. The girl saw her mother was in earnest, so she plied her distaff as well as she could; but her little hands were all untaught, and by the evening of the second day a very small part of her task was accomplished. She cried herself to sleep that night, and in the morning, throwing aside her work in despair, she strolled out into the fields, all sparkling with dew. At last she reached a flowery knoll, at whose foot ran a little burn, shaded with woodbine and wild roses; and there she sat down, burying her face in her hands. When she looked up, she was surprised to see by the margin of the stream an old woman, quite unknown to her, 'drawing out the thread' as she basked in the sun. There was nothing very remarkable in her appearance, except the length and thickness of her lips, only she was seated on a self-bored stone. The girl rose, went to the good dame, and gave her a

*From the Wilkie MS.

friendly greeting, but could not help inquiring what made her so 'long lippit'. 'Spinning thread, ma hinnie,' said the old woman, pleased with her friendliness, and by no means resenting the personal remark. It must be noticed that spinners used constantly to wet their fingers with their lips, as they drew the thread from the rock or distaff. 'Ah!' said the girl, 'I should be spinning too, but it's a' to no purpose, I sall ne'er do my task;' on which the old woman proposed to do it for her. Overjoyed, the maiden ran to fetch her lint, and placed it in her new friend's hand, asking her name, and where she should call for the yarn in the evening; but she received no reply; the old woman's form passed away from her among the trees and bushes, and disappeared. The girl, much bewildered, wandered about a little, sat down to rest, and finally fell asleep by the little knoll.

When she awoke she was surprised to find that it was evening. The glories of the western sky were passing into twilight grey. Causleen, the evening star, was beaming with silvery light, soon to be lost in the moon's increasing splendour. While watching these changes, the maiden was startled by the sound of an uncouth voice, which seemed to issue from below a self-bored stone, close beside her. She laid her ear to the stone, and distinctly heard these words: 'Little kens the wee lassie on yon brae-head that ma name's Habitrot.' Then, looking down the hole, she saw her friend, the old dame, walking backwards and forwards in a deep cavern among a group of spinsters all seated on colludie stones (a kind of white pebble found in rivers), and busy with distaff and spindle. An unsightly company they were, with lips more or less disfigured by their employment, as were old Habitrot's. The same peculiarity extended to another of the sisterhood, who sat in a distant corner reeling the yarn; and she was marked, in addition, by grey eyes, which seemed starting from her head, and a long hooked nose.

As she reeled, she counted thus, 'Ae cribbie, twa cribbie, haith cribbie thou's áne; ae cribbie, twa cribbie, haith cribbie thou's twa,' and so on. After this manner she continued till she had counted a cut, hank, slip – a cribbie being once round the reel, or a measure of about three feet, the reel being about eighteen inches long.

While the girl was still watching, she heard Habitrot address this singular being by the name of Scantlie Mab, and tell her to bundle up the yarn, for it was time the young lassie should give it to her mother. Delighted to hear this, our listener got up and turned homewards, nor was she long kept in suspense. Habitrot soon overtook her, and placed the yarn in her hands. 'Oh, what can I do for ye in return?' exclaimed she, in delight. 'Naething – naething,' replied the dame; 'but dinna tell yer mither whae spun the yarn.'

Scarcely crediting her good fortune, our heroine went home, where she found her mother had been busy making sausters, or black puddings, and hanging them up in the lum to dry, and then, tired out, had retired to rest. Finding herself very hungry after her long day on the knoll, the girl took down pudding after pudding, fried and ate them, and at last went to bed too. The mother was up first the next morning, and when she came into the kitchen and found her sausters all gone, and the seven hanks of yarn lying beautifully smooth and bright upon the table, her mingled feelings of vexation and delight were too much for her. She ran out of the house wildly, crying out –

> 'Ma daughter's spun se'en, se'en, se'en,
> Ma daughter's eaten se'en, se'en, se'en,
>   And all before daylight!'

A laird, who chanced to be riding by, heard the exclamation, but could not understand it; so he rode up and asked the gudewife what was the matter, on which she broke out again –

> 'Ma daughter's spun se'en, se'en, se'en,
> Ma daughter's eaten se'en, se'en, se'en

before daylight; and if ye dinna believe me, why come in and see it.' The laird's curiosity was aroused; he alighted and went into the cottage, where he saw the yarn, and admired it so much, he begged to see the spinner.

The mother dragged in the blushing girl. Her rustic grace soon won his heart, and he avowed he was lonely without a wife, and had long been in search of one who was a good spinner. So their troth was plighted, and the wedding took place soon afterwards, the bride stifling her apprehensions that she should not prove so deft at her spinning-wheel as her lover expected. And once more old Habitrot came to her aid. Whether the good dame, herself so notable, was as indulgent to all idle damsels does not appear – certainly she did not fail this little pet of hers. 'Bring your bonny bridegroom to my cell,' said she to the young bride soon after her marriage; 'he shall see what comes o'spinning, and never will he tie you to the spinning-wheel.'

Accordingly the bride led her husband the next day to the flowery knoll, and bade him look through the self-bored stone. Great was his surprise to behold Habitrot dancing and jumping over her rock,[1] singing all the time this

[1] Spinning-wheel.

ditty to her sisterhood, while they kept time with their
spindles:

> 'We who live in dreary den
>   Are both rank and foul to see,
> Hidden frae the glorious sun
>   That teems the fair earth's canopie:
> Ever must our evenings lone
> Be spent on the colludie stone.
>
> Cheerless is the evening grey
>   When Causleen hath died away,
> But ever bright and ever fair
>   Are they who breathe this evening air;
> And lean upon the self-bored stone
> Unseen by all but me alone.'

The song ended, Scantlie Mab asked Habitrot what she
meant by her last line, 'Unseen by all but me alone.' 'There
is ane,' replied Habitrot, 'whom I bid to come here at this
hour, and he has heard my song through the self-bored
stone.' So saying she rose, opened another door, which was
concealed by the roots of an old tree, and invited the bridal
pair to come in and see her family.

The laird was astonished at the weird-looking company,
as he well might be, and enquired of one after another the
cause of the strange distortion of their lips. In a different
tone of voice, and with a different twist of the mouth, each
answered that it was occasioned by spinning. At least they
tried to say so, but one grunted out, 'Nakasind,' and
another 'Owkasaänd,' while a third murmured 'O-a-a-
send.' All, however, conveyed the fact to the bridegroom's
understanding; while Habitrot slyly hinted that if his wife

were allowed to spin, her pretty lips would grow out of shape too, and her pretty face get an ugsome look. So before he left the cave he protested his little wife should never touch a spinning-wheel, and he kept his word. She used to wander in the meadows by his side, or ride behind him over the hills, and all the flax grown on his land was sent to old Habitrot to be converted into yarn.

THE TULMAN*

There was a woman in Baile Thangusdail, and she was out seeking a coupe of calves; and the night and lateness caught her, and there came rain and tempest, and she was seeking shelter. She went to a knoll with the couple of calves, and she was striking a tether-peg into it. The knoll opened. She heard a gleegashing as if a pot-hook were clashing beside a pot. She took wonder, and she stopped striking the tether-peg. A woman put out her head and all above her middle, and she said, 'What business hast thou to be troubling this tulman in which I make my dwelling?' 'I am taking care of this couple of calves, and I am but weak. Where shall I go with them?' 'Thou shalt go with them to that breast down yonder. Thou wilt see a tuft of grass. If thy couple of calves eat that tuft of grass, thou wilt not be a day without a milk cow as long as thou art alive, because thou hast taken my counsel.'

As she said, she never was without a milk cow after that, and she was alive fourscore and fifteen years after the night that was there.

*Campbell, *Popular Tales of the West Highlands*.

THE ISLE OF PABAIDH*

There came a woman of peace (a fairy) the way of the house of a man in the island of Pabaidh, and she had the hunger of motherhood on her. He gave her food, and that went well with her. She stayed that night. When she went away she said to him, 'I am making a desire that none of the people of this island may go in childbed after this.' None of these people, and none others that would make their dwelling in the island, ever departed in childbed from that time.

SANNTRAIGH†

There was a herd's wife in the island of Sanntraigh, and she had a kettle. A woman of peace would come every day to seek the kettle. She would not say a word when she came, but she would catch hold of the kettle. When she would catch the kettle, the woman of the house would say –

'A smith is able to make
Cold iron hot with coal.
The due of a kettle is bones,
And to bring it back again whole.'

The woman of peace would come back every day with the kettle, and flesh and bones in it. On a day that was there, the housewife was for going over the ferry to Baile a Chaisteil, and she said to her man, 'If thou wilt say to the woman of peace as I say, I will go to Baile Castle.' 'Oo!

*Campbell, *Popular Tales of the West Highlands*.
†The same.

I will say it. Surely it's I that will say it.' He was spinning a heather rope to be set on the house. He saw a woman coming and a shadow from her feet, and he took fear of her. He shut the door. He stopped his work. When she came to the door she did not find the door open, and he did not open it for her. She went above a hole that was in the house. The kettle gave two jumps, and at the third leap it went out at the ridge of the house. The night came, and the kettle came not. The wife came back over the ferry, and she did not see a bit of the kettle within, and she asked, 'Where was the kettle?' 'Well, then, I don't care where it is,' said the man; 'I never took such a fright as I took at it. I shut the door, and she did not come any more with it.' 'Good-for-nothing wretch, what didst thou do? There are two that will be ill off – thyself and I.' 'She will come tomorrow with it.' 'She will not come.'

She hasted herself and she went away. She reached the knoll, and there was no man within. It was after dinner, and they were out in the mouth of the night. She went in. She saw the kettle, and she lifted it with her. It was heavy for her with the remnants that they left in it. When the old carle that was within saw her going out, he said –

> 'Silent wife, silent wife,
> That came on us from the land of chase,
> Thou man on the surface of the "Bruth",
> Loose the black, and slip the Fierce.'

The two dogs were let loose; and she was not long away when she heard the clatter of the dogs coming. She kept the remnant that was in the kettle, so that if she could get it with her, well, and if the dogs should come that she might throw it at them. She perceived the dogs coming. She put her hand in the kettle. She took the board out of it, and she threw at them a quarter of what was in it. They noticed it there for a while. She perceived them again, and she threw another piece at them when they closed upon her. She went away walking as well as she might; when she came near the farm, she threw the mouth of the pot downwards, and there she left them all that was in it. The dogs of the town struck up a barking when they saw the dogs of peace stopping. The woman of peace never came more to seek the kettle.

WATER FAIRIES*

The Dracæ are a sort of water-spirits who inveigle women and children into the recesses which they inhabit, beneath lakes and rivers, by floating past them, on the surface of the water, in the shape of gold rings or cups. The women thus seized are employed as nurses, and after seven years are permitted to revisit earth. Gervase of Tilbury mentions one woman in particular who had been allured by observing a wooden dish, or cup, float by her, while she was washing clothes in the river. Being seized as soon as she reached the depths, she was conducted into one of the subterranean recesses, which she described as very magnificent, and employed as nurse to one of the brood of the hag who had allured her. During her residence in this capacity, having accidentally touched one of her eyes with an ointment of serpent's grease, she perceived, at her return to the world, that she had acquired the faculty of seeing the *Dracæ*, when they intermingle themselves with men. Of this power she was, however, deprived by the

*Sir Walter Scott, *Minstrelsy of the Scottish Border*.

touch of her ghostly mistress, whom she had one day incautiously addressed. It is a curious fact that this story, in almost all its parts, is current in both the Highlands and Lowlands of Scotland, with no other variation than the substitution of Fairies for Dracæ, and the cavern of a hill for that of a river. Indeed many of the vulgar account it extremely dangerous to touch anything which they may happen to find without saining (blessing) it, the snares of the enemy being notorious and well-attested. A poor woman of Teviotdale having been fortunate enough, as she thought herself, to find a wooden beetle, at the very time when she needed such an implement, seized it without pronouncing a proper blessing, and, carrying it home, laid it above her bed to be ready for employment in the morning. At midnight the window of her cottage opened, and a loud voice was heard calling up some one within by a strange and uncouth name. The terrified cottager ejaculated a prayer, which, we may suppose, ensured her personal safety; while the enchanted implement of house-wifery, tumbling from the bedstead, departed by the window with no small noise and precipitation.

FAIRY TRANSPORTATION*

The power of the fairies was not confined to unchristened children alone; it was supposed frequently to be extended to full-grown persons, especially such as in an unlucky hour were devoted to the devil by the execration of parents and of masters; or those who were found asleep under a rock, or on a green hill, belonging to the fairies, after sunset, or, finally, to those who unwarily joined their orgies. A

*Sir Walter Scott, *Minstrelsy of the Scottish Border*.

tradition existed, during the seventeenth century, concerning an ancestor of the noble family of Duffus, who, 'walking abroad in the fields, near to his own house, was suddenly carried away, and found the next day at Paris, in the French king's cellar, with a silver cup in his hand. Being brought into the king's presence, and questioned by him who he was, and how he came thither, he told his name, his country, and the place of his residence! and that on such a day of the month, which proved to be the day immediately preceding, being in the fields, he heard the noise of a whirl-wind, and of voices, crying *"Horse and Hattock!"* (this is the word which the fairies are said to use when they remove from any place), whereupon he cried *"Horse and Hattock"* also, and was immediately caught up and transported through the air by the fairies, to that place, where, after he had drunk heartily, he fell asleep, and before he woke, the rest of the company were gone, and had left him in the posture wherein he was found. It is said the king gave him the cup which was found in his hand, and dismissed him.' The narrator affirms 'that the cup was still preserved, and known by the name of the *Fairy Cup*.' He adds that Mr Steward, tutor to the then Lord Duffus, had informed him that, 'when a boy at the school of Forres, he and his school-fellows were upon a time whipping their tops in the church-yard, before the door of the church, when, though the day was calm, they heard a noise of a wind, and at some distance saw the small dust begin to rise and turn round, which motion continued advancing till it came to the place where they were, whereupon they began to bless them-selves; but one of their number being, it seems, a little more bold and confident than his companions, said, *"Horse and Hattock with my top,"* and immediately they all saw the top lifted up from the ground, but could not see which way it was carried, by reason of a cloud of dust which was raised at the same time. They sought for the top all about the place where it was taken up, but in vain; and it was found afterwards in the churchyard, on the other side of the church.'

THE POOR MAN OF PEATLAW*

The following is an account of a fairy frolic said to have happened late in the last century: The victim of elfin sport was a poor man, who, being employed in pulling heather upon Peatlaw, a hill in Selkirkshire, had tired of his labour, and laid him down to sleep upon a fairy ring. When he awakened, he was amazed to find himself in the midst of a populous city, to which, as well as to the means of his transportation, he was an utter stranger. His coat was left upon the Peatlaw; and his bonnet, which had fallen off in the course of his aerial journey, was afterwards found hanging upon the steeple of the church of Lanark. The distress of the poor man was, in some degree, relieved by meeting a carrier, whom he had formerly known, and who conducted him back to Selkirk, by a slower conveyance than had whirled him to Glasgow. That he had been carried off by the fairies was implicitly believed by all who did not reflect that a man may have private reasons for leaving his own country, and for disguising his having intentionally done so.

*Sir Walter Scott, *Minstrelsy of the Scottish Border*.

THE FAIRY BOY OF LEITH*

The worthy Captain George Burton communicated to Richard Bovet, gentleman, author of the interesting work entitled *Pandœmonium, or the Devil's Cloister Opened*,[1] the following singular account of a lad called the Fairy Boy of Leith, who, it seems, acted as a drummer to the elves, who weekly held rendezvous in the Calton Hill, near Edinburgh.

'About fifteen years since, having business that detained me for some time at Leith, which is near Edinburgh, in the kingdom of Scotland, I often met some of my acquaintance at a certain house there, where we used to drink a glass of wine for our refection; the woman which kept the house was of honest reputation among the neighbours, which made me give the more attention to what she told me one day about a fairy boy (as they called him), who lived about that town. She had given me so strange an acccount of him that I desired her I might see him the first opportunity, which she promised; and not long after, passing that way, she told me there was the fairy boy but a little before I came by; and, casting her eye into the street, said, Look you, sir, yonder he is at play with those other boys; and designing him to me, I went, and, by smooth words, and a piece of money, got him to come into the house with me; where, in the presence of divers people, I demanded of him several astrological questions, which he answered with great subtilty; and, through all his discourse, carried it with a cunning much above his years, which seemed not to exceed ten or eleven.

*Sir Walter Scott, *Minstrelsy of the Scottish Border*.
[1]London, 1684.

'He seemed to make a motion like drumming upon the table with his fingers, upon which I asked him whether he could beat a drum? To which he replied, Yes, sir, as well as any man in Scotland; for every Thursday night I beat all points to a sort of people that used to meet under yonder hill (pointing to the great hill between Edenborough and Leith). How, boy? quoth I, what company have you there? There are, sir, said he, a great company both of men and women, and they are entertained with many sorts of musick, besides my drum; they have, besides, plenty of variety of meats and wine, and many times we are carried into France or Holland in a night, and return again, and whilst we are there we enjoy all the pleasures the country doth afford. I demanded of him how they got under that hill? To which he replied that there was a great pair of gates that opened to them, though they were invisible to others; and that within there were brave large rooms, as well accommodated as most in Scotland. I then asked him how I should know what he said to be true? Upon which he told me he would read my fortune, saying I should have two wives, and that he saw the forms of them sitting on my shoulders; that both would be very handsome women. As he was thus speaking, a woman of the neighbourhood, coming into the room, demanded of him what her fortune should be? He told her that she had two bastards before she was married, which put her in such a rage that she desired not to hear the rest.

'The woman of the house told me that all the people in Scotland could not keep him from the rendezvous on Thursday night; upon which, by promising him some more money, I got a promise of him to meet me at the same place, in the afternoon, the Thursday following, and so dismist him at that time. The boy came again, at the place and time appointed, and I had prevailed with some friends to continue with me, if possible, to prevent his moving that night. He was placed between us, and answered many questions, until, about eleven of the clock, he was got away unperceived by the company; but I, suddenly missing him, hasted to the door, and took hold of him, and so returned him into the same room; we all watched him, and, of a sudden, he was again got out of doors; I followed him close, and he made a noise in the street, as if he had been set upon; but from that time I could never see him.

'GEORGE BURTON'

'MIND THE CROOKED FINGER'*

Bill Robertson, æt. 71, residing in Lerwick, soberly narrated this trowy story:

'My midder, God rest her soul, tauld me this, and she nedder could nor wid ha' tauld me a lee. Shü wis staying wi' freends at Kirgood-a-Weisdale; an' ee nicht about da hüming (twilight) da guidman was sair fashed, for da honest wife haed just haed a pirie baby. An' noo, my lamb 'at ye ir (are), what sud he hear juist as he was gaein' ta leave the lamb-house, but three most unearthly knocks, da sam as it haed a been frae onder da grund. Noo, he kent na what dis could be, but he made a' fast, an' gangs up intil de corn yard, and as he comes in sight of the screws he hears a voice 'at said tree times, "Mind da crooked finger." Noo, his wife haed a crooked finger, and he kent ower weel 'at something wis gaen ta happen, for his *grey neebors* wis apon da watch for da helpless infant, or midder, or baith. So he comes into da hoose, an' lichts a candle, taks doon da Bible, an' a steel

*Mr J. G. Ollason's MS.

knife. He opens da buik an' da knife, when such a roaring and *trüling*, an' onerthly stamping an' rattling, an' confusion comes frae da byre as made da whole hoose shak. An' a' body fell a-whaaking (quaking). Noo, he taks da open Bible, and maks for da byre, an' dem 'at wis i' da hoos follows him trimbling an' whaaking, only da wise-woman bein' left with da poor wife an' infant. Noo, whin he gets ta da door, he heaves in da Bible afore him, sticks da open knife in his mouth, edge ootwards, and da lowin' candle in een o' his hands. Da instant yon was dune da trülin' an' noise an' din ceased all of a sudden, and da image 'at haed been prepared for ta pit i' da place i' da poor wife an' innocent pirie lamb was a' 'at was left i' da byre. "Weel," says da guidman, as he gripped in his airms da very likeness o' his wife 'at da trows had left i' da byre, "I've taen dee, and I'll use dee." Weel, he tuk in ta da hoose da image left by da trows, an' it haed every joint an' pairt of a woman. An' my midder tauld me shü saw it, an' da honest folk for mony a year, an' der children after dem, sat upon da stock, or image, or likness; an' things was set on it, and wood was sawn on it. An' dat's as true as I'm spekin' to you, and no a borrowed or handed story; for my midder tauld me it wi' her ain lips, an' she wid no a tauld me a lee.'

THE TWO YOUNG PLOUGHMEN*

'You have been often at the Gatehouse,' said Johnny Nicholson; 'well, you'll mind a flat piece of land near Enrick farm; well, that was once a large loch; a long way down from there is still the ruin of a mill, which at that time was fed from this loch. Well, one night about the

*Campbell, *Popular Tales of the West Highlands*.

Hallowe'en times, two young ploughmen went to a smiddy to get their socks (of their ploughs) and colters repaired, and in passing the said mill on their way home again they heard music and dancing, and fiddling, and singing, and laughing, and talking; so one of the lads would be in to see what was going on; the other waited outside for hours, but his companion never came out again, so he went home, assured that the brownies had got hold of him. About the same time the following year, the same lad went again to the smiddy on the same errand, and this time he took another lad with him, but had the precaution to put the Bible in his pocket. Well, in passing the mill the second time, he heard the same sounds of music and dancing. This time, having the Bible in his hand, he ventured to look in, when who should he see but his companion whom he had left standing there that day twelvemonths. He handed him the Bible, and the moment he did so the music and dancing ceased, the lights went out, and all was darkness.'

THE SMITH AND THE FAIRIES*

Years ago there lived in Crossbrig a smith of the name of MacEachern. This man had an only child, a boy of about thirteen or fourteen years of age, cheerful, strong, and healthy. All of a sudden he fell ill, took to his bed, and moped whole days away. No one could tell what was the matter with him, and the boy himself could not, or would not, tell how he felt. He was wasting away fast; getting thin, old, and yellow; and his father and all his friends were afraid that he would die.

At last one day, after the boy had been lying in this

*Campbell, *Popular Tales of the West Highlands*.

condition for a long time, getting neither better nor worse, always confined to bed, but with an extraordinary appetite – one day, while sadly revolving these things, and standing idly at his forge, with no heart to work, the smith was agreeably surprised to see an old man, well known to him for his sagacity and knowledge of out-of-the-way things, walk into his workshop. Forthwith he told him the occurrence which had clouded his life.

The old man looked grave as he listened; and after sitting a long time pondering over all he had heard, gave his opinion thus – 'It is not your son you have got. The boy has been carried away by the "Daoine Sith", and they have left a *Sibhreach* in his place.' 'Alas! and what then am I to do?' said the smith. 'How am I ever to see my own son again ?'

'I will tell you how,' answered the old man. 'But, first, to make sure that it is not your own son you have got, take as many empty egg-shells as you can get, go with them into the room, spread them out carefully before his sight, then proceed to draw water with them, carrying them two and two in your hands as if they were a great weight, and arrange when full, with every sort of earnestness, round the fire.' The smith accordingly gathered as many broken egg-shells as he could get, went into the room, and proceeded to carry out all his instructions.

He had not been long at work before there arose from the bed a shout of laughter, and the voice of the seeming sick boy exclaimed, 'I am now 800 years of age, and I have never seen the like of that before.'

The smith returned and told the old man. 'Well, now,' said the sage to him, 'did I not tell you that it was not your son you had: your son is in Brorra-cheill in a digh there (that is, a round green hill frequented by fairies). Get rid as soon as possible of this intruder, and I think I may promise you your son.

'You must light a very large and bright fire before the bed on which this stranger is lying. He will ask you, "What is the use of such a fire as that?" Answer him at once, "You will see that presently!" and then seize him, and throw him into the middle of it. If it is your own son you have got, he will call out to save him; but if not, this thing will fly through the roof.'

The smith again followed the old man's advice; kindled a large fire, answered the question put to him as he had been directed to do, and seizing the child flung him without hesitation. The 'Sibhreach' gave an awful yell, and sprung through the roof, where a hole was left to let the smoke out.

On a certain night the old man told him the green round hill, where the fairies kept the boy, would be open. And on that night the smith, having provided himself with a Bible, a dirk, and a crowing cock, was to proceed to the hill. He would hear singing and dancing and much merriment going on, but he was to advance boldly; the Bible he carried would be a certain safeguard to him against any danger from the fairies. On entering the hill he was to stick the dirk in the threshold, to prevent the hill from closing upon him; 'and then,' continued the old man, 'on entering you will see a spacious apartment before you, beautifully clean, and there, standing far within, working at a forge, you will also see your own son. When you are questioned, say you come to seek him, and will not go without him.'

Not long after this the time came round, and the smith sallied forth, prepared as instructed. Sure enough, as he approached the hill, there was a light where light was seldom seen before. Soon after a sound of piping, dancing, and joyous merriment reached the anxious father on the night wind.

Overcoming every impulse to fear, the smith approached the threshold steadily, stuck the dirk into it as directed, and entered. Protected by the Bible he carried on his breast, the fairies could not touch him; but they asked him, with a good deal of displeasure, what he wanted there. He answered, 'I want my son, whom I see down there, and I will not go without him.'

Upon hearing this the whole company before him gave a loud laugh, which wakened up the cock he carried dozing in his arms, who at once leaped up on his shoulders, clapped his wings lustily, and crowed loud and long.

The fairies, incensed, seized the smith and his son, and, throwing them out of the hill, flung the dirk after them, and in an instant all was dark.

For a year and a day the boy never did a turn of work, and hardly ever spoke a word; but at last one day, sitting by his father and watching him finishing a sword he was making for some chief, and which he was very particular about, he suddenly exclaimed, 'That is not the way to do it;' and, taking the tools from his father's hands, he set to work himself in his place, and soon fashioned a sword the like of which was never seen in the country before.

From that day the young man wrought constantly with his father, and became the inventor of a peculiarly fine and well-tempered weapon, the making of which kept the two smiths, father and son, in constant employment, spread their fame far and wide, and gave them the means in abundance, as they before had the disposition, to live content with all the world and very happily with one another.

THE LOTHIAN FARMER'S WIFE*

The wife of a farmer in Lothian had been carried off by the fairies, and, during the year of probation, repeatedly appeared on Sunday, in the midst of her children, combing their hair. On one of these occasions she was accosted by her husband; when she related to him the unfortunate event which had separated them, instructed him by what means he might *win* her, and exhorted him to exert all his courage, since her temporal and eternal happiness depended on the success of his attempt. The farmer, who ardently loved his wife, set out on Hallowe'en, and, in the midst of a plot of furze, waited impatiently for the procession of the fairies. At the ringing of the fairy bridles, and the wild, unearthly sound which accompanied the cavalcade, his heart failed him, and he suffered the ghostly train to pass by without interruption. When the last had rode past, the whole troop vanished, with loud shouts of laughter and exultation; among which he plainly discovered the voice of his wife, lamenting that he had lost her for ever.

REDEMPTION FROM FAIRY LAND†

Near the town of Aberdeen, in Scotland, lived James Campbell, who had one daughter, named Mary, who was married to John Nelson, a young man of that neighbourhood. Shortly after their marriage, they being a young couple, they went to live in the town of Aberdeen, where he followed his trade, being a goldsmith; they lived loving and agreeable together until the time of her lying-in, when there

*Sir Walter Scott, *Minstrelsy of the Scottish Border*.
†Sir Walter Scott, *ibid.*, 'from a broadside still popular in Ireland.'

was female attendants prepared suitable to her situation; when near the hour of twelve at night they were alarmed with a dreadful noise, at which of a sudden the candles went out, which drove the attendants in the utmost confusion; soon as the women regained their half-lost senses, they called in their neighbours, who, after striking up lights, and looking towards the lying-in woman, found her a corpse, which caused great confusion in the family. There was no grief could exceed that of her husband, who next morning, prepared ornaments for her funeral; people of all sects came to her wake, amongst others came the Rev. Mr Dodd, who, at first sight of the corpse, said, 'It's not the body of any Christian, but that Mrs Nelson was taken away by the fairies, and what they took for her was only some substance left in her place.' He was not believed, so he refused attending her funeral; they kept her in the following night, and the next day she was interred.

Her husband, one evening after sunset, being riding in his own field, heard a most pleasant concert of music, and soon after espied a woman coming towards him dressed in white; she being veiled, he could not observe her face, yet he rode near her, and asked very friendly who she was that chose to walk alone so late in the evening? at which she unveiled her face, and burst into tears, saying, I am not permitted to tell you who I am. He knowing her to be his wife, asked her in the name of God, what disturbed her, or what occasioned her to appear at that hour? She said her appearing at any hour was of no consequence; for though you believe me to be dead and buried, I am not, but was taken away by the fairies the night of my delivery; you only buried a piece of wood in my place; I can be recovered if you take proper means; as for my child, it, has three nurses to attend it, but I fear it cannot be brought home; the greatest dependence I have on any person is my brother Robert, who is a captain of a merchant ship, and will be home in ten days hence. Her husband asked her what means he should take to win her? She told him he should find a letter the Sunday morning following, on the desk in his own room, directed to her brother, wherein there would be directions for winning her. Since my being taken from you I have had the attendance of a queen or empress, and if you look over my right shoulder you will see several of my companions; he then did as she desired, when, at a small distance, he saw a king and queen sitting, beside a moat,[1] on a throne, in splendour.

She then desired him to look right and left, which he did, and observed other kings on each side of the king and queen, well guarded. He said, I fear it is an impossibility to win you from such a place. No, says she, were my brother Robert here in your place, he would bring me home; but let it not encourage you to attempt the like, for that would occasion the loss of me for ever; there is now severe punishment threatened to me for speaking to you; but, to prevent that, do you ride up to the moat, where (suppose you will see no person) all you now see will be near you, and do you threaten to burn all the old thorns and brambles that is round the moat, if you do not get a firm promise that I shall get no punishment; I shall be forgiven; which he promised. She then disappeared, and he lost sight of all he had seen; he then rode very resolutely up to the moat, and went round it, vowing he would burn all about it if he would not get a promise that his wife should get no hurt. A voice desired him to cast away a book that was in his pocket, and then demand his request; he answered he would not part with his book, but grant his request, or they should find the

[1] A rising ground, a knoll.

effect of his rage. The voice answered, that upon honour she should be forgave her fault, but for him to suffer no prejudice to come to the moat, which he promised to fulfil, at which he heard most pleasant music. He then returned home, and sent for the Rev. Mr Dodd, and related to him what he had seen; Mr Dodd stayed with him till Sunday morning following, when as Mr Nelson looked on the desk in his room, he espied a letter, which he took up, it being directed to her brother, who in a few days came home; on his receiving the letter he opened it, wherein he found the following:

'DEAR BROTHER – My husband can relate to you my present circumstances. I request that you will (the first night after you see this) come to the moat where I parted from my husband: let nothing daunt you, but stand in the centre of the moat at the hour of twelve at night, and call me, when I, with several others, will surround you; I shall have on the whitest dress of any in company; then take held of me, and do not forsake me; all the frightful methods they shall use let it not surprise you, but keep your hold, suppose they continue till cock crow, when they shall vanish all of a sudden, and I shall be safe, when I will return home and live with my husband. If you succeed in your attempt, you will gain applause from all your friends, and have the blessing of your ever-loving and affectionate sister,

'MARY NELSON'

No sooner had he read the letter than he vowed to win his sister and her child, or perish in the attempt; he returned to the ship, and related to his sailors the contents of the letter; he delayed till ten at night, when his loyal sailors offered to go with him, which he refused, thinking it best to go alone. As he left his ship a frightful lion came roaring towards him; he drew his sword and struck at the lion, which he observed was of no substance, it being only the appearance of one, to terrify him in his attempt; it only encouraged him, so that he proceeded to the moat, in the centre of which he observed a white handkerchief spread; on which he was surrounded with a number of women, the cries of whom were the most frightful he ever heard; his sister being in the whitest dress of any round him, he seized her by the right hand, and said, With the help of God, I will preserve you from all infernal imps: when of a sudden, the moat seemed to be on fire around him. He likewise heard the most dreadful thunder could be imagined; frightful birds and beasts seemed to make towards him out of the fire, which he knew was not real; nothing daunted his courage; he kept hold of his sister for the space of an hour and three-quarters, when the cocks began to crow; then the fire disappeared, and all the frightful imps vanished. He held her in his arms, and fell on his knees, and gave God thanks for his proceedings that night: he believing her clothing to be light, put his outside coat on her: she then embraced him, saying she was now safe, as he put any of his clothing on her; he then brought her home to her husband, which occasioned great rejoicing. Her husband and he began to conclude to destroy the moat in revenge of the child they had away, when instantly they heard a voice, which said, you shall have your son safe, and well, on condition that you will not till the ground within three perches of the moat, nor damage bushes or brambles round that place, which they agreed to, when, in a few minutes, the child was left on his mother's knee, which caused them to kneel and return thanks to God.

The circumstance of this terrifying affair was occasioned by leaving Mrs Nelson, the night of her lying-in, in the care of women who were mostly intoxicated with liquor!

THE FAIRY AND THE BIBLE-READER*

On a still Sabbath evening in summer, an old man was seated, reading his Bible in the open air, at a quiet spot upon the Ross-shire coast. A beautiful little lady, clad in green, drew near, and addressing him in a silvery voice, sought to know if for such as she Holy Scripture held out any hope of salvation. The old man spoke kindly to her; but said that in those pages there was no mention of salvation for any but the sinful sons of Adam. On hearing this, the fairy flung her arms despairingly above her head, and with a shriek plunged into the sea.

THOM AND WILLIE†

Thom and Willie, two young fisher-mates of Lunna, in Shetland, were rivals for the hand of the fair Osla, daughter of Jarm. Now it so happened that, one October afternoon, they took their hand-lines and went out fishing together in their boat. Towards dusk the wind rose, and it soon blew so hard as to compel the young men to run for the nearest shelter – a haven in the islet of Linga in Whalsay Sound, which they happily reached in safety. The islet was uninhabited, and the fishermen had with them neither food nor the means of kindling a fire. They had, however, a roof

*Campbell, *Popular Tales of the* West *Highlands*.
†Arranged from Mr J. G. Ollason's MS.

over their heads; for there was a hut, or lodge, on the island, used by fishermen in the fair weather season, but deserted since the close of that period. For two days the storm raged without ceasing, and at last the situation of the castaways began to grow very serious. However, on the morning of the third day, a little before daybreak, Willie, who was awake before his companion, discovered that the weather had faired, and that the wind blew in a favouring direction. Upon this, without rousing Thom, he proceeded to the boat, which lay safely hauled up upon the shore, and by dint of great exertion managed to launch her single-handed. Meantime Thom had awoke; and, at last, as Willie did not come back, he followed him to the noust, or place where boats are drawn up. And here a sight met his view which filled him with dismay. The yawl had disappeared from her place; but, raising his eyes, he beheld her already far out at sea and speeding before the breeze in the direction of Lunna. At this sight poor Thom gave way to despair. He realised that his comrade had basely and heartlessly deserted him; he knew that it was not likely that the islet would be visited until the fishing-season should have come round again; and he had small hopes of help from any exertions on his behalf which might be made by his friends, seeing that they would be in ignorance where to look for him. Amid melancholy thoughts and forebodings the day passed slowly, and at nightfall he betook himself to his shake-down of straw within the lodge. Darkness closed in, and he slept. But, towards the small hours of the morning, he was suddenly awakened; when great was his astonishment to see that the hut was lighted up with a strange illumination, whilst a queer inhuman hum and chatter, accompanied by the patter of many pairs of little feet and the jingle of gold and silver vessels, smote upon his ear. A fairy banquet was, in fact, in course of preparation in the lodge. Thom raised himself noiselessly upon his elbow, and watched the proceedings. With infinite bustle and clatter, the table was at last laid. Then there entered a party of trows, who bore between them in a chair, or litter, a female fairy, to whom all appeared to pay honour. The company took seats, and the banquet was on the point of commencing, when in a moment the scene of festivity was changed to one of wild alarm and confusion. A moment more, and Thom learnt to his cost the cause of the sudden change. The presence of a human being had been detected, and at a word from their queen the 'grey people', swarming together, were about to rush upon the intruder. But in this trying juncture Thom did not lose his presence of mind. His loaded fowling-piece lay by his side, and, as the fairies rushed upon him, he raised it to his shoulder and fired. In an instant the light was extinguished, and all was darkness, silence, and solitude.

Let us now return to the perfidious Willie. Reaching Lunna in safety, he related a tragic tale (which he had invented on the voyage), to account for the absence of his comrade; and, finding that his story was believed, he began anew, without much loss of time, to urge his suit with the fair Osla. Her father, Jarm, regarded him with favour; but the maiden herself turned a deaf ear to all his entreaties. She felt that she could not love him; and, besides, she was haunted by a suspicion that Thom, in whose welfare she felt a tender interest, had been the victim of foul play. Pressure was, however, put upon her, and in spite of her objections, an early day was fixed for the wedding. The poor girl was in great distress. However, one night, when she had cried herself to sleep, she dreamed a dream, the result of which was that next morning she proceeded to the house of Thom's parents, and begged them to join her in a search for their missing son. This, notwithstanding their love for him, they were somewhat reluctant to do; arguing that, even supposing him to have been abandoned, as she divined, upon one of the rocky islets of the coast, he must ere now have perished from exposure and starvation. But the girl persisted in her entreaties, which at last prevailed. A boat was manned, and by Osla's direction was steered towards Linga, upon approaching which, sure enough, as the girl had predicted, it was discovered that the islet had a human tenant. Thom met his friends on the beach, and when the first eager greetings had passed, surprise was expressed at the freshness and robustness of his appearance. But this surprise increased tenfold when, in recounting his adventures, he explained that, during the latter days of his isolation, he had supported life upon the remains of the scarcely-tasted fairy banquet, adding that never in his life before had he fared so delicately. On their return to Lunna, the party were received with rejoicings; and it is scarcely necessary to add that Thom and Osla were soon made man and wife. From that time forward Willie prospered no more. The loss of his health and fortune followed that of his good name, and he sank ere long into an early and unregretted grave.

THE GLOAMING BUCHT*

'Speakin' o' fairies,' quoth Robbie Oliver (an old shepherd, who lived at Southdean in Jedwater, and died about 1830), 'I can tell ye about the vera last fairy that was seen hereaway. When my faither, Peter Oliver, was a young man,
*Old Friends with Newe Faces. Field & Tuer.

he lived at Hyndlee, an' herdit the Brocklaw. Weel, it was the custom to milk the yowes in thae days, an' my faither was buchtin'[1] the Brocklaw yowes to twae young, lish, clever hizzies ae nicht i' the gloamin'. Nae little daffin' an' gabbin'[2] gaed on amang the threesome, I'se warrant ye, till at last, just as it chanced to get darkish, my faither chancit to luik alang the lea at the head o' the bucht, an' what did he see but a wee little creaturie a' clad i' green, an' wi' lang hair, yellow as gowd, hingin' round its shoulders, comin' straight for him, whiles gi'en a whink o' a greet,[3] an' aye atween its hands raisin' a queer, unyirthly cry, "Hae ye seen Hewie Milburn? Oh! hae ye seen Hewie Milburn?" Instead of answering the creature, my faither sprang owre the bucht flake,[4] to be near the lasses, saying, "Bliss us a' – what's that?" "Ha, ha! Patie lad," quo' Bessie Elliot, a free-spoken Liddesdale hempy; "theer a wife com'd for ye the nicht, Patie lad." "A wife !" said my faither; "may the Lord keep me frae sic a wife as that," an' he confessed till his deein' day, he was in sic a fear that the hairs o' his heed stuid up like the birses of a hurcheon.[5] The creature was nae bigger than a three-year-auld lassie, but feat an' tight, lith o' limb, as ony grown woman, an' its face was the downright perfection o' beauty, only there was something wild an' unyirthly in its e'en that couldna be lookit at, faur less describit: it didna molest them, but aye taigilt[6] on about the bucht, now an' then repeatin' its cry, "Hae ye seen Hewie Milburn?" Sae they cam' to nae ither conclusion than that it had tint[7] its companion. When my faither an' the lasses left the bucht, it followed them hame to the Hyndlee kitchen, where they offered it yowe brose, but it wad na tak' onything, till at

---

[1]Folding.
[2]Romping and 'chaffing'.
[3]Whimper.
[4]Movable gate of the fold.
[5]Bristles of a hedgehog.
[6]Lingered.
[7]Lost.

last a neer-do-weel callant made as if he wad grip it wi'
a pair o' reed-het tangs, an' it appeared to be offendit,
an' gaed awa' doon the burnside, cryin' its auld cry eerier
an' waesomer than ever, and disappeared in a bush o'
seggs.'[1]

THE FAIRY'S SONG[2]

'O where is tiny Hew?
  And where is little Len?
And where is bonnie Lu,
  And Menie of the Glen?
And where's the place of rest –
  The ever changing hame?
Is it the gowan's breast,
  Or 'neath the bells of faem?
    Ay lu lan dil y'u.

'The fairest rose you find
  May have a taint within;
The flower of womankind
  May not be free from sin –
The foxglove cup go bring,
  The tail of shooting sterne,
And round our grassy ring
  We'll pledge the pith o' fern.
    Ay lu lan dil y'u.

[1]Sedge.
[2]The song is taken from a poem founded upon the above story, and
entitled the *Gloamyne Buchte*. The author was James Telfer, schoolmaster
at Saughtree, in Liddesdale; born 1800, died 1862.

'And when the yellow moon
　　Is gliding down the sky,
On wings of wishes boun',
　　Our band to her can fly;
Her highest horn we'll ride,
　　And quaff her honey dew;
Then in her shadowy side
　　Our gambollings renew!
　　　Ay lu lan dil y'u.'

THE BROWNIE, THE BOGLE,
THE KELPY,
MERMEN, DEMONS

The Brownie, the Bogle, the Kelpy, Mermen, Demons

THE SCOTTISH BROWNIE*

The Scottish Brownie formed a class of beings distinct in habit and disposition from the freakish and mischievous elves. He was meagre, shaggy, and wild in his appearance.

In the daytime he lurked in remote recesses of the old houses which he delighted to haunt; and in the night sedulously employed himself in discharging any laborious task which he thought might be acceptable to the family to whose service he had devoted himself. But the Brownie does not drudge from the hope of recompense. On the contrary, so delicate is his attachment that the offer of reward, but particularly of food, infallibly occasions his disappearance for ever. It is told of a Brownie, who haunted a Border family now extinct, that the lady having fallen unexpectedly in labour, and the servant, who was ordered to ride to Jedburgh for the *sage-femme*, showing no great alertness in setting out, the familiar spirit slipt on the great-coat of the

*Sir Walter Scott, *Minstrelsy of the Scottish Border*.

lingering domestic, rode to the town on the laird's best horse, and returned with the midwife *en croupe*. During the short space of his absence, the Tweed, which they must necessarily ford, rose to a dangerous height. Brownie, who transported his charge with all rapidity, was not to be stopped by this obstacle. He plunged in with the terrified old lady, and landed her in safety where her services were wanted. Having put the horse into the stable (where it was afterwards found in a woful plight), he proceeded to the room of the servant whose duty he had discharged, and, finding him just in the act of drawing on his boots, administered to him a most merciless drubbing with his own horsewhip. Such an important service excited the gratitude of the laird, who, understanding that Brownie had been heard to express a wish to have a green coat, ordered a vestment of that colour to be made and left in his haunts. Brownie took away the green coat, but was never seen more. We may suppose that, tired of his domestic drudgery, he went in his new livery to join the fairies.

THE BROWNIE OF BODSBECK*

The brownie of the farmhouse of Bodsbeck, in Moffatdale, left his employment upwards of a century ago, on a similar account. He had exerted himself so much in the farm-labour, both in and out of doors, that Bodsbeck became the most prosperous farm in the district. He always took his meat as it pleased himself, usually in very moderate quantities, and of the most humble description. During a time of very hard labour, perhaps harvest, when a little better fare than ordinary might have been judged acceptable, the goodman

*Chambers, *Popular Rhymes of Scotland*.

took the liberty of leaving out a mess of bread and milk, thinking it but fair that at a time when some improvement, both in quantity and quality, was made upon the fare of the human servants, the useful brownie should obtain a share in the blessing. He, however, found his error, for the result was that the brownie left the house for ever, exclaiming –

'Ca', brownie, ca'
A' the luck o' Bodsbeck away to Leithenha'.'

The luck of Bodsbeck accordingly departed with its brownie, and settled in the neighbouring farmhouse, called Leithenhall, whither the brownie transferred his friendship and services.

THE BROWNIE AND THE THIEVISH MAIDS*

One of the principal characteristics of the brownie was his anxiety about the moral conduct of the household to which he was attached. He was a spirit very much inclined to prick up his ears at the first appearance of any impropriety in the manners of his fellow-servants. The least delinquency committed either in barn, or cow-house, or larder, he was sure to report to his master, whose interests he seemed to consider paramount to every other thing in this world, and from whom no bribe could induce him to conceal the offences which fell under his notice. The men, therefore, and not less the maids, of the establishment usually regarded him with a mixture of fear, hatred, and respect; and though he might not often find occasion to do his duty as a spy, yet the firm belief that he would be relentless in

*Chambers, *Popular Rhymes of Scotland*.

doing so, provided that he did find occasion, had a salutary effect. A ludicrous instance of his zeal as guardian of the household morals is told in Peeblesshire. Two dairymaids, who were stinted in their food by a too frugal mistress, found themselves one day compelled by hunger to have recourse to the highly improper expedient of stealing a bowl of milk and a bannock, which they proceeded to devour, as they thought, in secret. They sat upon a form, with a space between, whereon they placed the bowl and the bread, and they took *bite and sip* alternately, each putting down the bowl upon the seat for a moment's space after taking a draught, and the other then taking it up in her hands, and treating herself in the same way. They had no sooner commenced their mess than the brownie came between the two, invisible, and whenever the bowl was set down upon the seat took also a draught; by which means, as he devoured fully as much as both put together, the milk was speedily exhausted. The surprise of the famished girls at finding the bowl so soon empty was extreme, and they began to question each other very sharply upon the subject, with mutual suspicion of unfair play, when the brownie undeceived them by exclaiming, with malicious glee –

'Ha! ha! ha!
Brownie has 't a'!'

THE BOGLE*

This is a freakish spirit, who delights rather to perplex and frighten mankind than either to serve or seriously to hurt them. *Shellycoat*, a spirit who resides in the waters, and has

*Sir Walter Scott, *Minstrelsy of the Scottish Border*.

given his name to many a rock and stone upon the Scottish coast, belongs to the class of bogles. When he appeared, he seemed to be decked with marine productions, and in particular with shells, whose clattering announced his approach. From this circumstance he derived his name. One of his pranks is thus narrated: Two men, on a very dark night, approaching the banks of the Ettrick, heard a doleful voice from its waves repeatedly exclaim, 'Lost! Lost!' They followed the sound, which seemed to be the voice of a drowning person, and, to their infinite astonishment, they found that it ascended the river. Still they continued, during a long and tempestuous night, to follow the cry of the malicious sprite and arriving, before morning's dawn, at the very sources of the river, the voice was now heard descending the opposite side of the mountain in which they arise. The fatigued and deluded travellers now relinquished the pursuit, and had no sooner done so than they heard Shellycoat applauding, in loud bursts of laughter, his successful roguery. The spirit was supposed particularly to haunt the old house of Gorinberry, situated on the river Hermitage, in Liddesdale.

THE DOOMED RIDER*

'The Conan is as bonny a river as we hae in a' the north country. There's mony a sweet sunny spot on its banks, an' 'mony a time an' aft hae I waded through its shallows, whan a boy, to set my little scauting-line for the trouts an' the eels, or to gather the big pearl-mussels that lie sae thick in the fords. But its bonny wooded banks are places for enjoying the day – no for passing the nicht. I kenna how it

*Folk-Lore and Legends, Scotland. W. W. Gibbings.

is; it's nane o' your wild streams that wander desolate through a desert country, like the Aven, or that come rushing down in foam and thunder, ower broken rocks, like the Foyers, or that wallow in darkness, deep, deep in the bowels o' the earth, like the fearfu' Auldgraunt; an' yet no ane o' these rivers has mair or frightfuller stories connected wi' it than the Conan. Ane can hardly saunter ower half-a-mile in its course, frae where it leaves Contin till where it enters the sea, without passing ower the scene o' some frightful auld legend o' the kelpy or the water-wraith. And ane o' the most frightful looking o' these places is to be found among the woods of Conan House. Ye enter a swampy meadow that waves wi' flags an' rushes like a cornfield in harvest, an' see a hillock covered wi' willows rising like an island in the midst. There are thick mirk-woods on ilka side; the river, dark an' awesome, an' whirling round an' round in mossy eddies, sweeps away behind it; an' there is an auld burying-ground, wi' the broken ruins o' an auld Papist kirk, on the tap. Ane can see amang the rougher stanes the rose-wrought mullions of an arched window, an' the trough that ance held the holy water. About twa hunder years ago – a wee mair maybe, or a wee less, for ane canna be very sure o' the date o' thae old stories – the building was entire; an' a spot near it, whar the wood now grows thickest, was laid out in a corn-field. The marks o' the furrows may still be seen amang the trees.

'A party o' Highlanders were busily engaged, ae day in harvest, in cutting down the corn o' that field; an' just aboot noon, when the sun shone brightest an' they were busiest in the work, they heard a voice frae the river exclaim, "The hour but not the man has come." Sure enough, on looking round, there was the kelpy stan'in' in what they ca' a fause ford, just fornent the auld kirk. There is a deep black pool both aboon an' below, but i' the ford there's a bonny ripple, that shows, as ane might think, but little depth o' water; an' just i' the middle o' that, in a place where a horse might swim, stood the kelpy. An' it again repeated its words, "The hour but not the man has come," an' then flashing through the water like a drake, it disappeared in the lower pool. When the folk stood wondering what the creature might mean, they saw a man on horseback come spurring down the hill in hot haste, making straight for the fause ford. They could then understand her words at ance; an' four o' the stoutest o' them sprang oot frae amang the corn to warn him o' his danger, an' keep him back. An' sae they tauld him what they had seen an' heard, an' urged him either to turn back an' tak' anither road, or stay for an hour or sae where he was. But he just wadna hear them, for he was baith unbelieving an' in haste, an' wauld hae taen the ford for a' they could say, hadna the Highlanders, determined on saving him whether he would or no, gathered round him an' pulled him frae his horse, an' then, to mak' sure of him, locked him up in the auld kirk. Weel, when the hour had gone by – the fatal hour o' the kelpy – they flung open the door, an' cried to him that he might noo gang on his journey. Ah! but there was nae answer, though; an' sae they cried a second time, an' there was nae answer still; and then they went in, an' found him lying stiff an' cauld on the floor, wi' his face buried in the water o' the very stone trough that we may still see amang the ruins. His hour had come, an' he had fallen in a fit, as 'twould seem, head-foremost amang the water o' the trough, where he had been smothered – an' sae ye see, the prophecy o' the kelpy availed naething.'

GRAHAM OF MORPHIE*

The old family of the Grahams of Morphie was in former times very powerful, but at length they sunk in fortune, and finally the original male line became extinct. Among the old women of the Mearns, their decay is attributed to a supernatural cause. When one of the lairds, say they, built the old castle, he secured the assistance of the water-kelpy or river-horse, by the accredited means of throwing a pair of branks[1] over his head. He then compelled the robust spirit to carry prodigious loads of stones for the building, and did not relieve him till the whole was finished. The poor kelpy was glad of his deliverance, but at the same time felt himself so galled with the hard labour, that on being permitted to escape from the branks, and just before he disappeared in the water, he turned about, and expressed, in the following words, at once his own grievances and the destiny of his taskmaster's family –

> 'Sair back and sair banes,
> Drivin' the laird o' Morphie's stanes!
> The laird o' Morphie 'll never thrive
> As lang's the kelpy is alive!'

THE FISHERMAN AND THE MERMAN†

Of mermen and merwomen many strange stories are told in the Shetland Isles. Beneath the depths of the ocean, according to these stories, an atmosphere exists adapted to

*Chambers, *Popular Rhymes of Scotland*.
†*Folk-Lore and Legends, Scotland*. W. W. Gibbings.
[1]Shafts.

the respiratory organs of certain beings, resembling in form the human race, possessed of surpassing beauty, of limited supernatural powers, and liable to the incident of death. They dwell in a wide territory of the globe, far below the region of fishes, over which the sea, like the cloudy canopy of our sky, loftily rolls, and they possess habitations constructed of the pearl and coral productions of the ocean. Having lungs not adapted to a watery medium, but to the nature of atmospheric air, it would be impossible for them to pass through the volume of waters that intervenes between the submarine and supramarine world, if it were not for the extraordinary power they inherit of entering the skin of some animal capable of existing in the sea, which they are enabled to occupy by a sort of demoniacal possession. One shape they put on is that of an animal human above the waist, yet terminating below in the tail and fins of a fish, but the most favourite form is that of the larger seal or Haaf-fish; for, in possessing an amphibious nature, they are enabled not only to exist in the ocean, but to land on some rock, where they frequently lighten themselves of their sea-dress, resume their proper shape, and with much curiosity examine the nature of the upper world belonging to the human race. Unfortunately, however, each merman or merwoman possesses but one skin, enabling the individual to ascend the seas, and if, on visiting the abode of man, the garb be lost, the hapless being must unavoidably become an inhabitant of the earth.

A story is told of a boat's crew who landed for the purpose of attacking the seals lying in the hollows of the crags at one of the stacks. The men stunned a number of the animals, and while they were in this state stripped them of their skins, with the fat attached to them. Leaving the carcases on the rock, the crew were about to set off for the

shore of Papa Stour, when such a tremendous swell arose
that every one flew quickly to the boat. All succeeded in
entering it except one man, who had imprudently lingered
behind. The crew were unwilling to leave a companion to
perish on the skerries,[1] but the surge increased so fast that
after many unsuccessful attempts to bring the boat close in
to the stack the unfortunate wight was left to his fate. A
stormy night came on, and the deserted Shetlander saw no
prospect before him but that of perishing from cold and
hunger, or of being washed into the sea by the breakers
which threatened to dash over the rocks. At length he
perceived many of the seals, who in their flight had escaped
the attack of the boatmen, approach the skerry, disrobe
themselves of their amphibious hides, and resume the shape
of the sons and daughters of the ocean. Their first object
was to assist in the recovery of their friends, who, having
been stunned by clubs, had, while in that state, been
deprived of their skins. When the flayed animals had
regained their sensibility, they assumed their proper form of
mermen or merwomen, and began to lament in a mournful
lay, wildly accompanied by the storm that was raging
around, the loss of their sea-dress, which would prevent
them ftom again enjoying their native azure atmosphere
and coral mansions that lay below the deep waters of the
Atlantic. But their chief lamentation was for Ollavitinus,
the son of Gioga, who, having been stripped of his seal's
skin, would be for ever parted from his mates, and
condemned to become an outcast inhabitant of the upper
world. Their song was at length broken off by observing
one of their enemies viewing, with shivering limbs and
looks of comfortless despair, the wild waves that dashed
over the stack. Gioga immediately conceived the idea of

[1]Rocks which are submerged at high tide.

rendering subservient to the advantage of her son the perilous situation of the man. She addressed him with mildness, proposing to carry him safe on her back across the sea to Papa Stour, on condition of receiving the seal-skin of Ollavitinus. A bargain was struck, and Gioga clad herself in her amphibious garb; but the Shetlander, alarmed at the sight of the stormy main that he was to ride through, prudently begged leave of the matron, for his better preservation, that he might be allowed to cut a few holes in her shoulders and flanks, in order to procure, between the skin and the flesh, a better fastening for his hands and feet. The request being complied with, the man grasped the neck of the seal, and committing himself to her care, she landed him safely at Acres Gio in Papa Stour; from which place he immediately repaired to a skeo[1] at Hamna Voe, where the skin was deposited, and honourably fulfilled his part of the contract by affording Gioga the means whereby her son could again revisit the ethereal space over which the sea spread its green mantle.

THE MERMAID WIFE*

A story is told of an inhabitant of Unst, who, in walking on the sandy margin of a voe,[2] saw a number of mermen and mermaids dancing by moonlight, and several seal-skins strewed beside them on the ground. At his approach they immediately fled to secure their garbs, and, taking upon themselves the form of seals, plunged immediately into the sea. But as the Shetlander perceived that one skin lay close

[1] Hut for drying fish.
[2] A deep inlet, or creek.
*Folk Lore and Legends, Scotland. W. Gibbings.

to his feet, he snatched it up, bore it swiftly away, and placed it in concealment. On returning to the shore he met the fairest damsel that was ever gazed upon by mortal eyes, lamenting the robbery, by which she had become an exile from her submarine friends, and a tenant of the upper world. Vainly she implored the restitution of her property; the man had drunk deeply of love, and was inexorable; but he offered her protection beneath his roof as his betrothed spouse. The merlady, perceiving that she must become an inhabitant of the earth, found that she could not do better than accept of the offer. This strange attachment subsisted for many years, and the couple had several children. The Shetlander's love for his merwife was unbounded, but his affection was coldly returned. The lady would often steal alone to the desert strand, and, on a signal being given, a large seal would make his appearance, with whom she would hold, in an unknown tongue, an anxious conference. Years had thus glided away, when it happened that one of the children, in the course of his play, found concealed beneath a stack of corn a seal's skin; and, delighted with the prize, he ran with it to his mother. Her eyes glistened with rapture – she gazed upon it as her own – as the means by which she could pass through the ocean that led to her native home. She burst forth into an ecstasy of joy, which was only moderated when she beheld her children, whom she was now about to leave; and, after hastily embracing them, she fled with all speed towards the seaside. The husband immediately returned, learned the discovery that had taken place, ran to overtake his wife, but only arrived in time to see her transformation of shape completed – to see her, in the form of a seal, bound from the ledge of a rock into the sea. The large animal of the same kind with whom she had held a secret converse soon appeared, and evidently congratulated he, in the most tender manner, on her escape. But before she dived to unknown depths, she cast a parting glance at the wretched Shetlander, whose despairing looks excited in her breast a few transient feelings of commiseration.

'Farewell!' said she to him, 'and may all good attend you. I loved you very well when I resided upon earth, but I always loved my first husband much better.'

THE SEAL-CATCHER'S ADVENTURE*

There was once upon a time a man who lived upon the northern coasts, not far from 'Taigh Jan Crot Callow' (John o' Groat's House), and he gained his livelihood by catching and killing fish, of all sizes and denominations. He had a particular liking for the killing of those wonderful beasts, half dog and half fish, called 'Roane', or seals, no doubt because he got a long price for their skins, which are not less curious than they are valuable. The truth is, that the most of these animals are neither dogs nor cods, but downright fairies, as this narration will show. It happened one day, as this notable fisher had returned from the prosecution of his calling, that he was called upon by a man who seemed a great stranger, and who said he had been despatched for him by a person who wished to contract for a quantity of seal-skins, and that the fisher must accompany him (the stranger) immediately to see the person who wished to contract for the skins, as it was necessary that he should be served that evening. Happy in the prospect of making a good bargain, and never suspecting any duplicity, he instantly complied. They both mounted a steed

*W. Grant Stewart, *Highland Superstitions and Amusements.*

belonging to the stranger, and took the road with such velocity that, although the direction of the wind was towards their backs, yet the fleetness of their movement made it appear as if it had been in their faces. On reaching a stupendous precipice which overhung the sea, his guide told him they had now reached their destination.

'Where is the person you spoke of?' inquired the astonished seal-killer.

'You shall see that presently,' replied the guide.

With that they immediately alighted, and, without allowing the seal-killer much time to indulge the frightful suspicions that began to pervade his mind, the stranger seized him with irresistible force, and plunged headlong with him into the sea. After sinking down, down, nobody knows how far, they at length reached a door, which, being open, led them into a range of apartments; filled with inhabitants – not people, but seals, who could nevertheless speak and feel like human folk; and how much was the seal-killer surprised to find that he himself had been unconsciously transformed into the like image. If it were not so, he would probably have died from the want of breath. The nature of the poor fisher's thoughts may be more easily conceived than described. Looking at the nature of the quarters into which he had landed, all hopes of escape from them appeared wholly chimerical, whilst the degree of comfort and length of life which the barren scene promised him were far from being flattering. The 'Roane', who all seemed in very low spirits, appeared to feel for him, and endeavoured to soothe the distress which he evinced by the amplest assurances of personal safety. Involved in sad meditation on his evil fate, he was quickly roused from his stupor by his guide's producing a huge gully or joctaleg,[1]

[1] A clasp-knife.

the object of which he supposed was to put an end to all his earthly cares. Forlorn as was his situation, however, he did not wish to be killed; and, apprehending instant destruction, he fell down, and earnestly implored for mercy. The poor generous animals did not mean him any harm, however much his former conduct deserved it, and he was accordingly desired to pacify himself, and cease his cries.

'Did you ever see that knife before?' said the stranger to the fisher.

The latter instantly recognised his own knife, which he had that day stuck into a seal, and with which it had escaped, and acknowledged it was formerly his own, for what would be the use of denying it?

'Well,' rejoined the guide, 'the apparent seal which made away with it is my father, who has lain dangerously ill ever since; and no means can stay his fleeting breath without your aid. I have been obliged to resort to the artifice I have practised to bring you hither, and I trust that my filial duty to my father will readily excuse me.'

Having said this, he led into another apartment the trembling seal-killer, who expected every minute to be punished for his own ill-treatment of the father. There he found the identical seal with which he had had the encounter in the morning, suffering most grievously from a tremendous cut in its hind-quarter. The seal-killer was then desired, with his hand, to cicatrise the wound, upon doing which it immediately healed, and the seal arose from its bed in perfect health. Upon this the scene changed from mourning to rejoicing – all was mirth and glee. Very different, however, were the feelings of the unfortunate seal-catcher, who expected no doubt to be metamorphosed into a seal for the remainder of his life. However, his late guide accosting him, said –

'Now, sir, you are at liberty to return to your wife and family, to whom I am about to conduct you; but it is on this express condition, to which you must bind yourself by a solemn oath – that you will never maim or kill a seal in all your life-time hereafter.'

To this condition, hard as it was, he joyfully acceded; and the oath being administered in all due form, he bade his new acquaintance most heartily and sincerely a long farewell. Taking hold of his guide, they issued from the place, and swam up till they regained the surface of the sea, and, landing at the said stupendous pinnacle, they found their former steed ready for a second canter. The guide breathed upon the fisher, and they became like men. They mounted their horse, and fleet as had been their course towards the precipice, their return from it was doubly swift; and the honest seal-killer was laid down at his own door-cheek, where his guide made him such a present as would have almost reconciled him to another similar expedition – such as rendered his loss of profession, in so far as regarded the seals, a far less intolerable hardship than he had at first considered it.

THE MERMAID OF KNOCKDOLION*

The old house of Knockdolion stood near the water of Girvan, with a black stone at the end of it. A mermaid used to come from the water at night, and taking her seat upon this stone, would sing for hours, at the same time combing her long yellow hair. The lady of Knockdolion found that this serenade was an annoyance to her baby, and she thought proper to attempt getting quit of it, by causing the

*Chambers, *Popular Rhymes of Scotland*.

stone to be broken by her servants. The mermaid, coming next night, and finding her favourite seat gone, sang thus –

'Ye may think on your cradle – I'll think on my stane;
And there'll never be an heir to Knockdolion again.'

Soon after, the cradle was found overturned, and the baby dead under it. It is added that the family soon after became extinct.

THE YOUNG LAIRD OF LORNTIE*

The young Laird of Lorntie, in Forfarshire, was one evening returning from a hunting excursion, attended by a single servant and two greyhounds, when, in passing a solitary lake, which lies about three miles south from Lorntie, and was in those times closely surrounded with natural wood, his ears were suddenly assailed by the shrieks of a female apparently drowning. Being of a fearless character, he instantly spurred his horse forward to the side of the lake, and there saw a beautiful female struggling with the water, and, as it seemed to him, just in the act of sinking. 'Help, help, Lorntie!' she exclaimed. 'Help, Lorntie – help, Lor—' and the waters seemed to choke the last sounds of her voice as they gurgled in her throat. The laird, unable to resist the impulse of humanity, rushed into the lake, and was about to grasp the long yellow locks of the lady, which lay like hanks of gold upon the water, when he was suddenly seized behind, and forced out of the lake by his servant, who, farther-sighted than his master, perceived the whole affair to be the feint of a water-spirit.

*Chambers, *Popular Rhymes of Scotland*.

'Bide, Lorntie – bide a blink!' cried the faithful creature, as the laird was about to dash him to the earth; 'that wauling madam was nae other, God sauf us! than the mermaid.' Lorntie instantly acknowledged the truth of this asseveration, which, as he was preparing to mount his horse, was confirmed by the mermaid raising herself half out of the water, and exclaiming, in a voice of fiendish disappointment and ferocity –

> 'Lorntie, Lorntie,
> Were it na your man,
> I had gart your heart's bluid
> Skirl[1] in my pan.'

NUCKELAVEE*

Nuckelavee was a monster of unmixed malignity, never willingly resting from doing evil to mankind. He was a spirit in flesh. His home was the sea; and whatever his means of transit were in that element, when he moved on land he rode a horse as terrible in aspect as himself. Some thought that rider and horse were really one, and that this was the shape of the monster. Nuckelavee's head was like a man's, only ten times larger, and his mouth projected like that of a pig, and was enormously wide. There was not a hair on the monster's body, for the very good reason that he had no skin.

If crops were blighted by sea-gust or mildew, if live stock fell over high rocks that skirt the shores, or if an epidemic raged among men, or among the lower animals,

[1]Sing.

*Mr W. Traill Dennison in the *Scottish Antiquary*.

Nuckelavee was the cause of all. His breath was venom, falling like blight on vegetable, and with deadly disease on animal life. He was also blamed for long-continued droughts; for some unknown reason he had serious objections to fresh water, and was never known to visit the land during rain.

I knew an old man who was credited with having once encountered Nuckelavee, and with having made a narrow escape from the monster's clutches. This man was very reticent on the subject. However, after much higgling and persuasion, the following narrative was extracted:

Tammas, like his namesake Tam o' Shanter, was out late one night. It was, though moonless, a fine starlit night. Tammas's road lay close by the sea-shore, and as he entered a part of the road that was hemmed in on one side by the sea, and on the other by a deep fresh-water loch, he saw some huge object in front of, and moving towards him. What was he to do? He was sure it was no earthly thing that was steadily coming towards him. He could not go to either side, and to turn his back to an evil thing he had heard was the most dangerous position of all; so Tammie said to himself, 'The Lord be aboot me, an' tak' care o' me, as I am oot on no evil intent this night!' Tammie was always regarded as rough and foolhardy. Anyway, he determined, as the best of two evils, to face the foe, and so walked resolutely yet slowly forward. He soon discovered to his horror that the gruesome creature approaching him was no other than the dreaded Nuckelavee. The lower part of this terrible monster, as seen by Tammie, was like a great horse with flappers like fins about his legs, with a mouth as wide as a whale's, from whence came breath like steam from a brewing-kettle. He had but one eye, and that as red as fire. On him sat, or rather seemed to grow from his back, a huge man with no legs, and arms that reached nearly to the ground. His head was as big as a clue of simmons (a clue of straw ropes, generally about three feet in diameter), and this huge head kept rolling from one shoulder to the other as if it meant to tumble off. But what to Tammie appeared most horrible of all, was that the monster was skinless; this utter want of skin adding much to the terrific appearance of the creature's naked body – the whole surface of it showing only red raw flesh, in which Tammie saw blood, black as tar, running through yellow veins, and great white sinews, thick as horse tethers, twisting, stretching, and contracting as the monster moved. Tammie went slowly on in mortal terror, his hair on end, a cold sensation like a film of ice between his scalp and his skull, and a cold sweat bursting from every pore. But he knew it was useless to flee, and he said, if he had to die, he would rather see who killed him than die with his back to the foe. In all his terror Tammie remembered what he had heard of Nuckelavee's dislike to fresh water, and, therefore, took that side of the road nearest to the loch. The awful moment came when the lower part of the head of the monster got abreast of Tammie. The mouth of the monster yawned like a bottomless pit. Tammie found its hot breath like fire on his face: the long arms were stretched out to seize the unhappy man. To avoid, if possible, the monster's clutch, Tammie swerved as near as he could to the loch; in doing so one of his feet went into the loch, splashing up some water on the foreleg of the monster, whereat the horse gave a snort like thunder and shied over to the other side of the road, and Tammie felt the wind of Nuckelavee's clutches as he narrowly escaped the monster's grip. Tammie saw his opportunity, and ran with all his might; and sore need had he to run, for Nuckelavee had turned and was galloping

after him, and bellowing with a sound like the roaring of
the sea. In front of Tammie lay a rivulet, through which the
surplus water of the loch found its way to the sea; and
Tammie knew, if he could only cross the running water, he
was safe; so he strained every nerve. As he reached the near
bank another clutch was made at him by the long arms.
Tammie made a desperate spring and reached the other
side, leaving his bonnet in the monster's clutches.
Nuckelavee gave a wild unearthly yell of disappointed rage
as Tammie fell senseless on the safe side of the water.

THE TWO SHEPHERDS*

There were out between Lochaber and Baideanach two
shepherds who were neighbours to each other, and the one
would often be going to see the other. One was on the east
side of a river, and another on the west. The one who was
on the west side of the river came to the house of the one
who was on the east of it on an evening visit. He stayed till
it was pretty late, and then he wished to go home. 'It is
time to go home,' said he. 'It is not that which thou shalt
do, but thou shalt stay tonight,' said the other, 'since it is
so long in the night.' 'I will not stay at all events; if I were
over the river I don't care more.' The houseman had a
pretty strong son, and he said, 'I will go with thee, and I
will set thee over the river, but thou hadst better stay.' 'I
will not stay at all events.' 'If thou wilt not stay I will go
with thee.' The son of the houseman called a dog which he
had herding. The dog went with him. When he set the man
on the other side of the river, the man said to him, 'Be
returning now; I am far in thy debt.' The strong lad

*Campbell, *Popular Tales of the West Highlands.*

returned, and the dog with him. When he reached the river as he was returning back home, he was thinking whether he should take the stepping-stones, or put off his foot-clothes and take below. He put off his foot-clothes for fear of taking the stepping-stones, and when he was over there in the river the dog that was with him leaped at the back of his head. He threw her off him; she leaped again; he did the same thing. When he was on the other side of the river he put his hand on his head, and there was not a bit of a bonnet on it. He was saying, whether should he return to seek the bonnet, or should he go home without it. 'It's disgusting for me to return home without my bonnet; I will return over yet to the place where I put my foot-clothes off me; I doubt it is there that I left it.' So he returned to the other side of the river. He saw a right big man seated where he had been, and his own bonnet in his hand. He caught hold of the bonnet, and he took it from him. 'What business hast thou there with that? – It is mine, and thou hadst no business to take it from me, though thou hast got it.' Over the river then they went, without a word for each other, fiercely, hatingly. When they went over, then, on the river, the big man put his hand under the arm of the shepherd, and he began to drag the lad down to a loch that was there, against his will and against his strength. They stood front to front, bravely, firmly on either side. In spite of the strength of the shepherd's son, the big man was about to conquer. It was so that the shepherd's son thought of putting his hand about an oak tree that was in the place. The big man was striving to take him with him, and the tree was bending and twisting. At last the tree was loosening in the earth. She loosened all but one of her roots. At the time when the last root of the tree slipped, the cocks that were about the wood crowed. The shepherd's son understood when he heard the cocks crowing that it was on the short side of day. When they heard between them the cocks crowing, the big man said, 'Thou hast stood well, and thou hadst need, or thy bonnet had been dear for thee.' The big man left him, and they never more noticed a thing near the river.

FATLIPS*

About fifty years ago, an unfortunate female wanderer took up her residence in a dark vault, among the ruins of Dryburgh Abbey, which, during the day, she never quitted. When night fell, she issued from this miserable habitation, and went to the house of Mr Haliburton, of Newmains, or to that of Mr Erskine, of Shielfield, two gentlemen of the neighbourhood. From their charity she obtained such necessaries as she could be prevailed upon to accept. At twelve, each night, she lighted her candle, and returned to her vault; assuring her friendly neighbours that, during her absence, her habitation was arranged by a spirit, to whom she gave the uncouth name of *Fatlips,* describing him as a little man, wearing heavy iron shoes, with which he trampled the clay floor of the vault, to dispel the damps. This circumstance caused her to be regarded, by the well-informed, with compassion, as deranged in her understanding; and by the vulgar, with some degree of terror. The cause of her adopting this extraordinary mode of life she would never explain. It was, however, believed to have been occasioned by a vow that, during the absence of a man to whom she was attached, she would never look upon the sun. Her lover never returned. He fell during the civil war

*Sir Walter Scott, *Minstrelsy of the Scottish Border.*

of 1745–6, and she never more would behold the light of day.

The vault, or rather dungeon, in which this unfortunate woman lived and died, passes still by the name of the supernatural being with which its gloom was tenanted by her disturbed imagination, and few of the neighbouring peasants dare enter it by night.

WITCHCRAFT

Witchcraft

MACGILLICHALLUM OF RAZAY*

John Garve MacGillichallum, of Razay, was an ancient hero of great celebrity. Distinguished in the age in which he lived for the gallantry of his exploits, he has often been selected by the bard as the theme of his poems and songs. Alongst with a constitution of body naturally vigorous and powerful, Razay was gifted with all those noble qualities of the mind which a true hero is supposed to possess. And what reflected additional lustre on his character was that he never failed to apply his talents and powers to the best uses. He was the active and inexorable enemy of the weird sisterhood, many of whom he was the auspicious instrument of sending to their 'black inheritance' much sooner than they either expected or desired. It was not therefore to be supposed that, while those amiable actions endeared Razay to all good people, they were at all calculated to win him the regard of those infernal hags to whom he was so deadly a foe. As might be naturally expected, they cherished towards him the most implacable thirst of revenge, and

*W. Grant Stewart, *Highland Superstitions*.

sought, with unremitting vigilance, for an opportunity of quenching it. That such an opportunity did unhappily occur, and that the meditated revenge of these hags was too well accomplished, will speedily appear from this melancholy story.

It happened upon a time that Razay and a number of friends planned an expedition to the island of Lewis, for the purpose of hunting the deer of that place. They accordingly embarked on board the chieftain's yacht, manned by the flower of the young men of Razay, and in a few hours they chased the fleet-bounding hart on the mountains of Lewis. Their sport proved excellent. Hart after hart, and hind after hind, were soon levelled to the ground by the unerring hand of Razay; and when night terminated the chase they retired to their shooting quarters, where they spent the night with joviality and mirth, little dreaming of their melancholy fate in the morning.

In the morning of next day, the chief of Razay and his followers rose with the sun, with the view of returning to Razay. The day was squally and occasionally boisterous, and the billows raged with great violence. But Razay was determined to cross the channel to his residence, and ordered his yacht to prepare for the voyage. The more cautious and less courageous of his suite, however, urged on him to defer the expedition till the weather should somewhat settle, an advice which Razay, with a courage which knew no fear, rejected, and expressed his firm determination to proceed without delay. Probably with a view to inspire his company with the necessary degree of courage to induce them all to concur in the undertaking, he adjourned with them to the ferry-house where they had recourse to that supporter of spirits under every trial, the usquebaugh, a few bottles of which added vastly to the resolution of the company. Just as the party were disputing the practicability of the proposed adventure, an old woman, with wrinkled front, bending on a crutch, entered the ferry-house; and Razay, in the heat of argument, appealed to the old woman, whether the passage of the channel on such a day was not perfectly practicable and free from danger. The woman, without hesitation, replied in the affirmative, adding such observations, reflecting on their courage, as immediately silenced every opposition to the voyage and accordingly the whole party embarked in the yacht for Razay. But, alas! what were the consequences? No sooner were they abandoned to the mercy of the waves than the elements seemed to conspire to their destruction. All attempts to put back the vessel proved unavailing, and she was speedily driven out before the wind in the direction of Razay. The heroic chieftain laboured hard to animate his company, and to dispel the despair which began to seize them, by the most exemplary courage and resolution. He took charge of the helm, and in spite of the combined efforts of the sea, wind, and lightning, he kept the vessel steadily on her course towards the lofty point of Aird, in Skye. The drooping spirits of his crew began to revive, and hope began to smile upon them – when lo! to their great astonishment, a large cat was seen to climb the rigging. This cat was soon followed by another of equal size, and the last by a successor, until at length the shrouds, masts, and whole tackle were actually covered with them. Nor did the sight of all those cats, although he knew well enough their real character, intimidate the resolute Razay, until a large black cat, larger than any of the rest, appeared on the mast-head, as commander-in-chief of the whole legion. Razay, on observing him, instantly foresaw the result; he, however, determined to sell his life as dearly as possible, and immediately commanded an attack upon the cats; but, alas! it soon proved abortive. With a simultaneous effort the cats overturned the vessel on her leeward wale, and every soul on board was precipitated into a watery grave. Thus ended the glorious life of *Jan Garbh MacGillichallum*, of Razay, to the lasting regret of the brave clan Leod and all good people, and to the great satisfaction of the abominable witches who thus accomplished his lamentable doom.

THE WITCH OF LAGGAN*

The same day, another hero, celebrated for his hatred of witchcraft, was warming himself in his hunting hut, in the forest of Gaick, in Badenoch. His faithful hounds, fatigued with the morning chase, lay stretched on the turf by his side, his gun, that would not miss, reclined in the neuk of the bothy, the *skian dhu* of the sharp edge hung by his side, and these alone constituted his company. As the hunter sat listening to the howling storm as it whistled by, there entered at the door an apparently poor weatherbeaten cat, shivering with cold, and drenched to the skin. On observing her, the hairs of the dogs became erected bristles, and they immediately rose to attack the pitiable cat, which stood trembling at the door. 'Great hunter of the hills,' exclaims the poor-looking trembling cat, 'I claim your protection. I know your hatred to my craft, and perhaps it is just. Still spare, oh spare a poor jaded wretch, who thus flies to you for protection from the cruelty and oppression of her sisterhood.' Moved to compassion by her eloquent address, and disdaining to take advantage of his greatest enemy in such

*W. Grant Stewart, *Highland Superstitions*.

a seemingly forlorn situation, he pacified his infuriated dogs, and desired her to come forward to the fire and warm herself. 'Nay,' says she, 'in the first place, you will please bind with this long hair those two furious hounds of yours, for I am afraid they will tear my poor hams to pieces. I pray you, therefore, my dear sir, that you would have the goodness to bind them together by the necks with this long hair.' But the curious nature of the hair induced the hunter to dissemble a little. Instead of having bound his dogs with it, as he pretended, he threw it across a beam of wood which connected the couple of the bothy. The witch then, supposing the dogs securely bound, approached the fire, and squatted herself down as if to dry herself. She had not sitten many minutes, when the hunter could easily discover a striking increase in her size, which he could not forbear remarking in a jocular manner to herself. 'A bad death to you, you nasty beast,' says the hunter; 'you are getting very large.' 'Ay, ay,' replied the cat equally jocosely, 'as my hairs imbibe the heat, they naturally expand.' These jokes, however, were but a prelude to a more serious conversation. The cat, still continuing her growth, had at length attained a most extraordinary size – when, in the twinkling of an eye, she transformed herself into her proper likeness of the Goodwife of Laggan, and thus addressed him: 'Hunter of the Hills, your hour of reckoning is arrived. Behold me before you, the avowed champion of my devoted sisterhood, of whom MacGillichallum of Razay and you were always the most relentless enemies. But Razay is no more. His last breath is fled. He lies a lifeless corpse on the bottom of the main; and now, Hunter of the Hills, it is your turn.' With these words, assuming a most hideous and terrific appearance, she made a spring at the hunter. The two dogs, which she supposed securely bound by the infernal hair, sprung at her in her turn, and a most furious conflict ensued. The witch, thus unexpectedly attacked by the dogs, now began to repent of her temerity. 'Fasten, hair, fasten,' she perpetually exclaimed, supposing the dogs to have been bound by the hair; and so effectually did the hair *fasten,* according to her order, that it at last snapt the beam in twain. At length, finding herself completely overpowered, she attempted a retreat, but so closely were the hounds fastened in her breasts, that it was with no small difficulty she could get herself disengaged from them. Screaming and shrieking, the Wife of Laggan dragged herself out of the house, trailing after the dogs, which were fastened in her so closely that they never loosed their hold until she demolished every tooth in their heads. Then metamorphosing herself into the likeness of a raven, she fled over the mountains in the direction of her home. The two faithful dogs, bleeding and exhausted, returned to their master, and, in the act of caressing his hand, both fell down and expired at his feet. Regretting their loss with a sorrow only known to the parent who weeps over the remains of departed children, he buried his devoted dogs, and returned home to his family. His wife was not in the house when he arrived, but she soon made her appearance. 'Where have you been, my love?' inquired the husband. 'Indeed,' replies she, 'I have been seeing the Goodwife of Laggan, who has been just seized with so severe an illness that she is not expected to live for any time.' 'Ay! ay!' says he, 'what is the matter with the worthy woman?' 'She was all day absent in the moss at her peats,' replies the wife, 'and was seized with a sudden colic, in consequence of getting wet feet; and now all her friends and neighbours are expecting her demission.' 'Poor woman,' says the husband; 'I am sorry for her. Get me some dinner;

it will be right that I should go and see her also.' Dinner being provided and despatched, the hunter immediately proceeded to the house of Laggan, where he found a great assemblage of neighbours mourning, with great sincerity, the approaching decease of a woman whom they all had hitherto esteemed virtuous. The hunter, walking up to the sick woman's bed in a rage, proportioned to the greatness of its cause, stripped the sick woman of all her coverings. A shriek from the now exposed witch brought all the company around her. 'Behold,' says he, 'the object of your solicitude, who is nothing less than an infernal witch. Today, she informs me, she was present at the death of the Laird òf Razay, and only a few hours have elapsed since she attempted to make me share his fate. This night, however, she shall expiate her crime by the forfeiture of her horrid life.' Relating to the company the whole circumstances of her attack upon him, which were too well corroborated by the conclusive marks she bore on her person, the whole company were perfectly convinced of her criminality; and the customary punishment was about to he inflicted on her, when the miserable wretch addressed them as follows: 'My ill-requited friends, spare an old acquaintance, already in the agonies of death, from any further mortal degradation. My crimes and my folly now stare me in the face, in their true colours; while my vile and perfidious seducer, the enemy of your temporal and spiritual interests, only laughs at me in my distress; and, as a reward for my fidelity to his interest, in seducing everything that was amiable, and in destroying everything that was good, he is now about to consign my soul to eternal misery. Let my example be a warning to all the people of the earth to shun the fatal rock on which I have split; and as a strong inducement for them to do so I shall atone for my iniquity to the utmost of my

ability by detailing to you the awful history of my life.'
Here the Wife of Laggan detailed at full length the way she
was seduced into the service of the Evil One – all the
criminal adventures in which she had been engaged, and
ended with a particular account of the death of
MacGillichallum of Razay, and her attack upon the hunter,
and then expired.

Meanwhile a neighbour of the Wife of Laggan was
returning home late at night from Strathdearn, where he
had been upon some business, and had just entered the
dreary forest of Monalea, in Badenoch, when he met a
woman dressed in black, who ran with great speed, and
inquired of the traveller, with great agitation, how far she
was distant from the churchyard of Dalarossie, and if she
could be there by twelve o'clock. The traveller told her she
might, if she continued to go at the same pace that she did
then. She then fled alongst the road, uttering the most
desponding lamentations, and the traveller continued his
road to Badenoch. He had not, however, walked many
miles when he met a large black dog, which travelled past
him with much velocity, as if upon the scent of a track or
footsteps; and soon after he met another large black dog
sweeping along in the same manner. The last dog, however,
was scarcely past, when he met a stout black man on a fine
fleet black courser, prancing along in the same direction
after the dogs. 'Pray,' says the rider to the traveller, 'did you
meet a woman as you came along the hill?' The traveller
replied in the affirmative. 'And did you meet a dog soon
after?' rejoined the rider. The traveller replied he did. 'And,'
added the rider, 'do you think the dog will overtake her ere
she can reach the church of Dalarossie?' 'He will, at any
rate, be very close upon her heels,' answered the traveller.
Each then took his own way. But before the traveller had

got the length of Glenbanchar, the rider overtook him on his return, with the foresaid woman before him across the bow of his saddle, and one of the dogs fixed in her breast, and another in her thigh. 'Where did you overtake the woman?' inquired the traveller. 'Just as she was entering the churchyard of Dalarossie,' was his reply. On the traveller's return home, he heard of the fate of the unfortunate Wife of Laggan, which soon explained the nature of the company he had met on the road. It was, no doubt, the spirit of the Wife of Laggan flying for protection from the infernal spirits (to whom she had sold herself), to the churchyard of Dalarossie, which is so sacred a place that a witch is immediately dissolved from all her ties with Satan on making a pilgrimage to it, either dead or alive. But it seems the unhappy Wife of Laggan was a stage too late.

THE BLACKSMITH'S WIFE OF YARROWFOOT*

Some years back, the blacksmith of Yarrowfoot had for apprentices two brothers, both steady lads, and, when bound to him, fine healthy fellows. After a few months, however, the younger of the two began to grow pale and lean, lose his appetite, and show other marks of declining health. His brother, much concerned, often questioned him as to what ailed him, but to no purpose. At last, however, the poor lad burst into an agony of tears, and confessed that he was quite worn-out, and should soon be brought to the grave through the ill-usage of his mistress, who was in truth a witch, though none suspected it. 'Every night,' he sobbed out, 'she comes to my bedside, puts a magic bridle on me, and changes me into a horse. Then, seated on my

*William Henderson, *Folk-Lore of the Northern Counties*.

back, she urges me on for many a mile to the wild moors, where she and I know not what other vile creatures hold their hideous feasts. There she keeps me all night, and at early morning I carry her home. She takes off my bridle, and there I am, but so weary I can ill stand. And thus I pass my nights while you are soundly sleeping.'

The elder brother at once declared he would take his chance of a night among the witches, so he put the younger one in his own place next the wall, and lay awake himself till the usual time of the witch-woman's arrival. She came, bridle in hand, and flinging it over the elder brother's head, up sprang a fine hunting horse. The lady leaped on his back, and started for the trysting-place, which on this occasion, as it chanced, was the cellar of a neighbouring laird.

While she and the rest of the vile crew were regaling themselves with claret and sack, the hunter who was left in a spare stall of the stable, rubbed and rubbed his head against the wall till he loosened the bridle, and finally got it off; on which he recovered his human form. Holding the bridle firmly in his hand, he concealed himself at the back of the stall till his mistress came within reach, when in an instant he flung the magic bridle over her head, and, behold, a fine grey mare! He mounted her and dashed off; riding through hedge and ditch, till, looking down, he perceived she had lost a shoe from one of her forefeet. He took her to the first smithy that was open, had the shoe replaced, and a new one put on the other forefoot, and then rode her up and down a ploughed field till she was nearly worn out. At last he took her home, and pulled the bridle off just in time for her to creep into bed before her husband awoke, and got up for his day's work.

The honest blacksmith arose, little thinking what had

been going on all night; but his wife complained of being very ill, almost dying, and begged him to send for a doctor. He accordingly aroused his apprentices; the elder one went out, and soon returned with one whom he had chanced to meet already abroad. The doctor wished to feel his patient's pulse, but she resolutely hid her hands, and refused to show them. The village Esculapius was perplexed; but the husband, impatient at her obstinacy, pulled off the bed-clothes, and found, to his horror, that horseshoes were tightly nailed to both hands! On further examination, her sides appeared galled with kicks, the same that the apprentice had given her during his ride up and down the ploughed field.

The brothers now came forward, and related all that had passed. On the following day the witch was tried by the magistrates of Selkirk, and condemned to be burned to death on a stone at the Bullsheugh, a sentence which was promptly carried into effect. It is added that the younger apprentice was at last restored to health by eating butter made from the milk of cows fed in kirkyards, a sovereign remedy for consumption brought on through being witch-ridden.

THE MILLER OF HOLDEAN*

While the miller of Holdean, in Berwickshire, was drying a melder[1] of oats, belonging to a neighbouring farmer, tired with the fatigues of the day, he threw himself down upon some straw in the kiln-barn, and soon fell fast asleep. After a time he was awakened by a confused noise, as if the

*W. Henderson, *Folk-Lore of the Northern Counties*.
[1]Grinding.

killogee[1] were full of people, all speaking together; on which he pulled aside the straw from the banks of the kiln, and, looking down, observed a number of feet and legs paddling among the ashes, as if enjoying the warmth from the scarcely extinguished fires. As he listened, he distinctly heard the words, 'What think ye o' my feeties?' – a second voice answering, 'An' what think ye o' mine?' Nothing daunted, though much astonished, the stout-hearted miller took up his 'beer mell', a large wooden hammer, and threw it down among them, so that the ashes flew about; while he cried out with a loud voice, 'What think ye o' my meikle mell amang a' thae legs o' yourn?' A hideous rout at once emerged from the kiln amid yells and cries, which passed into wild laughter; and finally these words reached the miller's ears, sung in a mocking tone:

> 'Mount and fly for Rhymer's tower,
> Ha, ha, ha, ha!
> The pawky[2] miller hath beguiled us,
> Or we wud hae stown[3] his luck
> For this seven years to come,
> And mickle water wud hae run
> While the miller slept.'

RONALDSON OF BOWDEN*

A man named Ronaldson, who lived at the village of Bowden, is reported to have had frequent encounters with

---

[1]The empty space before the fireplace in a kiln.
[2]Artful.
[3]Stolen.
*W. Henderson, *Folk-Lore of the Northern Counties*.

the witches of that place. Among these we find the following. One morning at sunrise, while he was tying his garter with one foot against a low dyke, he was startled at feeling something like a rope of straw passed between his legs, and himself borne swiftly away upon it to a small brook at the foot of the southernmost hill of Eildon. Hearing a hoarse smothered laugh, he perceived he was in the power of witches or sprites; and when he came to a ford called the Brig-o'-stanes, feeling his foot touch a large stone, he exclaimed, 'I' the name o' the Lord, ye'se get me no farther!' At that moment the rope broke, the air rang as with the laughter of a thousand voices; and as he kept his footing on the stone, he heard a muttered cry, 'Ah, we've lost the coof!'[1]

THE FARMER'S WIFE OF DELORAINE*

Witchcraft is not named in the next story, but we can scarcely be wrong in assuming it to be the agent at work in it. We must premise that it was, perhaps still is, customary in the Lowlands of Scotland, as in other secluded districts, for tailors to leave their workshops and go into the farm-houses of the neighbourhood to work by the day. The farmer's wife of Deloraine thus engaged a tailor with his workmen and apprentices for the day, begging them to come in good time in the morning. They did so, and partook of the family breakfast of porridge and milk. During the meal, one of the apprentices observed that the milk-jug was almost empty, on which the mistress slipt out of the backdoor with a basin in her hand to get a fresh

[1]Fool.

*W. Henderson, *Folk-Lore of the Northern Counties*.

supply. The lad's curiosity was roused, for he had heard there was no more milk in the house; so he crept after her, hid himself behind the door, and saw her turn a pin in the wall, on which a stream of pure milk flowed into the basin. She twirled the pin, and the milk stopped. Coming back, she presented the tailors with the bowl of milk, and they gladly washed down the rest of their porridge with it.

About noon, while our tailors were busily engaged with the gudeman's wardrobe, one of them complained of thirst, and wished for a bowl of milk like the morning's. 'Is that a'?' said the apprentice; 'ye'se get that.' The mistress was out of the way, so he left his work, found his way to the spot he had marked in the morning, twirled the pin, and quickly filled a basin. But, alas! he could not then stay the stream. Twist the pin as he would, the milk still continued to flow. He called the other lads, and implored them to come and help him; but they could only bring such tubs and buckets as they found in the kitchen, and these were soon filled. When the confusion was at its height, the mistress appeared among them, looking as black as thunder; whilst she called out, in a mocking voice, 'A'ye loons! ye hae drawn all the milk fra every coo between the head o' Yarrow an' the foot o't. This day ne'er a coo will gie her maister a drop o' milk, though he war gawing to starve.' The tailors slunk away abashed, and from that day forward the wives of Deloraine have fed their tailors on nothing but chappit 'taties and kale.

LAIRD HARRY GILLES*

The Laird Harry Gilles of Littledean was extremely fond of hunting. One day, as his dogs were chasing a hare, they

*W. Henderson, *Folk-Lore of the Northern Counties*.

suddenly stopped, and gave up the pursuit, which enraged him so much that he swore the animal they had been hunting must be one of the witches of Maxton. No sooner had he uttered the word than hares appeared all round him, so close that they even sprang over the saddle before his eyes, but still none of his hounds would give them chase. In a fit of anger he jumped off his horse and killed the dogs on the spot, all but one black hound, who at that moment turned to pursue the largest hare. Remounting his horse, he followed the chase, and saw the black hound turn the hare and drive it directly towards him. The hare made a spring as if to clear his horse's neck, but the laird dextrously caught hold of one of her fore-paws, drew out his hunting-knife, and cut it off; after which the hares, which had been so numerous, all disappeared. Next morning Laird Harry heard that a woman of Maxton had lost her arm in some unaccountable manner; so he went straight to her house, pulled out the hare's foot (which had changed in his pocket to a woman's hand and arm), and applied it to the stump. It fitted exactly. She confessed her crime, and was drowned for witchcraft the same day in the well, by the young men of Maxton.

THE MISSING WEB*

'Some time since, when calling at the house of one of my oldest parishioners, who had been a hand-loom weaver, he fell to speak of other days; and, amongst other things, he told me of the disappearance, some years back, on a fine summer's evening, of a web of linen which had been laid to

*W. Henderson, *Folk-Lore of the Northern Counties* (from the narrative of the Rev. R. O. Bromfield, of Sprouston).

bleach by the riverside at the foot of the glebe. The fisher
men, it seems, were "burning the water"[1] in the Skerry, and
the man who had charge of the web went off to see the
salmon "leistered", and on his return the web was gone. Of
course there was a sensation. The story was soon in everybody's mouth, with abundant suspicions of as many
persons as there were yards in the web of linen.

'The web belonged to a very important personage, no less
than the howdie, or old village midwife, who was not
disposed to sit down quietly under her loss. So she called in
the aid of a wise man from Leitholm, and next day told her
friend the weaver, my informant, that she had found the
thief, for the wise man had turned the key. The weaver
being anxious to see something of diablerie, the howdie
brought the wise man to his house; and the door being
locked on all within (four in number), the magician
proceeded as follows. He took a small key, and attached it
to a string, which he tied into the family Bible at a
particular place, leaving the key hanging out. Next he read
two chapters from the Bible, one of which was the history
of Saul and the witch of Endor; he then directed the howdie
and another person to support the key between them, on
the tips of their forefingers, and in that attitude the former
was told to repeat the names of all the suspected parties.

'Many persons were named, but the key still hung
between the fingers, when the wise man cried out, "Why
don't you say Jock Wilson?" This was accordingly done,
and immediately the key dropped, *i.e.*, turned off the finger-
ends. So the news spread far and wide that the thief was
discovered, for the key had been turned and Jock Wilson
was the man! He proved, however, not to be the man to
stand such imputations, and being without doubt an honest

[1]Spearing, or 'leistering', salmon by torch-light.

fellow, he declared "he wudna be made a thief by the deevil". So he went to consult a lawyer, but after many long discussions the matter died away; and my authority, the weaver, says it was believed the lawyer was bribed; "for he aye likit a dram."'

THE WITCHES OF DELNABO*

In the time of my grandmother, the farm of Delnabo was proportionally divided between three tenants. At first equally comfortable in their circumstances, it was in the course of some time remarked by all, and by none more forcibly than by one of the said three portioners, that, although superior in point of industry and talent to his two fellow-portioners, one of the tenants was daily lapsing into poverty, while his two neighbours were daily improving in estate. Amazed and grieved at the adverse fortune which thus attended his family, compared to the prosperous condition of his neighbours, the wife of the poor man was in the habit of expressing her astonishment at the circumstance, not only to her own particular friends, but likewise to the wives of her neighbours themselves.

On one of these occasions, the other two wives asked her what would she do to ameliorate her condition, if it were in her power? She answered them she would do anything whatever. (Here the other wives thought they had got a gudgeon that would snap at any bait, and immediately resolved to make her their confidante.) 'Well, then,' says one of the other two wives, 'if you agree to keep our communications strictly secret, and implicitly obey our instructions, neither poverty nor want shall ever assail you

W. Grant Stewart, *Highland Superstitions*.

more.' This speech of the other wife immediately impressed the poor man's wife with a strong suspicion of their real character. Dissembling all surprise at the circumstance, she promised to agree to all their conditions. She was then directed, when she went to bed that night, to carry along with her the floor broom, well known for its magical properties, which she was to leave by her husband's side in the course of the night, and which would represent her so exactly that the husband could not distinguish the difference in the morning. They at the same time enjoined her to discard all fears of detection, as their own husbands had been satisfied with those lovely substitutes (the brooms) for a great number of years. Matters being thus arranged, she was desired to join them at the hour of midnight, in order to accompany them to that scene which was to realise her future happiness.

Promising to attend to their instructions, the poor man's wife took leave of her neighbours, full of those sensations of horror which the discovery of such depravity was calculated to produce in a virtuous mind. Hastening home to her husband, she thought it no crime to break her promise to her wicked neighbours, and, like a dutiful and prudent wife, to reveal to the husband of her bosom the whole particulars of their interview. The husband greatly commended his wife's fidelity, and immediately entered into a collusion with her, which displays no ordinary degree of ingenuity. It was agreed that the husband should exchange apparel with the wife, and that he should, in this disguise, accompany the wives to the place appointed, to see what cantrips they intended to perform.

He accordingly arrayed himself in his wife's habiliments, and, at the hour of midnight, joined the party at the place appointed. The 'bride', as they called him, was most cordially received by the two Ladies of the Broom, who warmly congratulated the 'bride' upon *her* good fortune, and the speedy consummation of *her* happiness. He was then presented with a fir torch, a broom, and a riddle, articles with which they themselves were furnished. They directed their course along the banks of the rolling Avon, until they reached Craic-pol-nain, or the Craig of the Birds-pool. Here, in consequence of the steepness of the craig, they found it convenient to pass to the other side of the river. This passage they effected without the use of the navy, the river being fordable at the place. They then came in sight of Pol-nain, and lo! what human eye ever witnessed such a scene before! The pool appeared as if actually enveloped in a flame of fire. A hundred torches blazed aloft, reflecting their beams on the towering woods of Loynchork. And what ear ever heard such shrieks and yells as proceeded from the horrid crew engaged at their hellish orgies on Pol-nain? Those cries were, however, sweet music to the two wives of Delnabo. Every yell produced from them a burst of unrestrained pleasure, and away they frisked, leaving the amiable *bride* a considerable way behind. For the fact is, that he was in no hurry to reach the scene, and when he did reach it, it was with a determination to be only a spectator, and not a participator in the night's performance. On reaching the pool's side he saw what was going on – he saw abundance of hags steering themselves to and fro in their riddles, by means of their oars (the brooms), hallooing and skirling[1] worse than the bogles, and each holding in her left hand a torch of fir – whilst at other times they would swirl themselves into a row, and make profound obeisance to a large black ugly tyke,[2] perched on

[1]Shrieking.
[2]Dog.

a lofty rock, and who was no doubt the 'muckle thief' himself, and who was pleased to acknowledge most graciously those expressions of their loyalty and devotion, by bowing, grinning, and clapping his paws. Having adnministered to the *bride* some preliminary instructions, the impatient wives desired him to remain by the pool's side until they should commune with his Satanic Highness on the subject of *her* inauguration, directing *her*, as they proceeded on their voyage across the pool, to speed them in their master's name. To this order of the black pair the *bride* was resolved to pay particular attention. As soon as they were embarked in their riddles, and had wriggled themselves, by means of their brooms, into a proper depth of water, 'Go,' says he, 'in the name of the Best.' A horrid yell from the witches announced their instant fate – the magic spell was now dissolved – crash went the riddles, and down sank the two witches, never more to rise, amidst the shrieks and lamentations of the Old Thief and all his infernal crew, whose combined power and policy could not save them from a watery end. All the torches were extinguished in an instant, and the affrighted company fled in different directions, in such forms and similitudes as they thought most convenient for them to adopt; and the *wily bride* returned home at his leisure, enjoying himself vastly at the clever manner in which he had executed the instructions of his deceased friends. On arriving at his house, he dressed himself in his own clothes, and, without immediately satisfying his wife's curiosity at the result of his excursion, he yoked his cattle, and commenced his morning labours with as little concern as usual. His two neighbours, who were not even conscious of the absence of their wives (so ably substituted were they by the brooms), did the same. Towards breakfast-time, however, the two neighbours were not a little astonished that they observed no signs of their wives having risen from bed – notwithstanding their customary earliness – and this surprise they expressed to the *late bride,* their neighbour. The latter archly remarked that he had great suspicions, in his own mind, of their *rising* even that day. 'What mean you by that?' replied they. 'We left our wives apparently in good health when we ourselves arose.' 'Find them now,' was the reply – the *bride* setting up as merry a whistle as before. Running each to his bed, what was the astonishment of the husbands, when, instead of his wife, he only found an old broom? Their neighbour then told them that, if they chose to examine Pol-nain well, they would find both their dear doxies there. The grieving husbands accordingly proceeded thither, and with the necessary instruments dragged their late worthy partners to dry land, and afterwards privately interred them. The shattered vessels and oars of those unfortunate navigators, whirling about the pool, satisfied their lords of the manner by which they came to their ends and their names were no longer mentioned by their kindred in the land. It need scarcely be added that the poor man gradually recovered his former opulence; and that, in the course of a short time, he was comparatively as rich as he was formerly poor.

APPARITIONS, WRAITHS,
THE SECOND SIGHT

Apparitions, Wraiths,
The Second Sight

THE OLD LADY OF LITTLEDEAN*

The old tower of Littledean, on Tweedside, had long been haunted by the spirit of an old lady, once its mistress, who had been a covetous, grasping woman, and oppressive to the poor. Tradition averred that she had amassed a large sum of money by thrift or extortion, and now could not rest in her grave because of it. Spite of its ghost, however, Littledean Tower was inhabited by a laird and his family, who found no fault with their place of abode, and were not much troubled by thoughts of the supernatural world. One Saturday evening, however, a servant-girl, who was cleaning shoes in the kitchen by herself, suddenly observed an elf-light shining on the floor. While she gazed on it, it disappeared, and in its place stood an old woman wrapped in a brown cloak, who muttered something about being cold, and asked to warm herself at the fire. The girl readily consented, and seeing that her visitor's shoes were wet, and

*W. Henderson, *Folk-Lore of the Northern Counties.*

her toes peeping out blue and cold from their tips, she good-naturedly offered to dry and clean the shoes, and did so. The old lady, touched by this attention, confessed herself frankly to be the apparition that haunted the house. 'My gold wudna let me rest,' said she, 'but I'll tell ye where it lies; 'tis neath the lowest step o' the Tower stairs. Take the laird there, an' tell him what I now tell ye; then dig up the treasure, and put it in his hands. An' tell him to part it in two shares: one share let him keep, for he's master here now; the other share he maun part again, and gie half to you, for ye are a kind lassie and a true, and half he maun gie to the poor o' Maxton, the auld folk and the fatherless bairns, and them that need it most. Do this an' I sall rest in my grave, where I've no rested yet; and never will I trouble the house mair till the day o' doom.' The girl rubbed her eyes, looked again, and behold the old woman was gone!

Next morning the young servant took her master to the spot which had been indicated to her, and told him what had taken place. The stone was removed, and the treasure discovered, and divided according to the instructions given. The laird, being blessed with a goodly family of sturdy lads and smiling maidens, found no difficulty in disposing of his share. The servant-girl, so richly dowered, found a good husband ere the year had passed. The poor of Maxton, for the first time in their lives, blessed the old lady of Little-dean; and never was the ancient tower troubled again by ghost or apparition.

THE LADIES OF BOW-BRIG-SYKE*

The same locality supplies us with another legend. About half-a-mile to the east of Maxton, a small rivulet runs across the turnpike road, at a spot called Bow-brig-syke. Near this bridge lies a triangular field, in which, for nearly a century, it was averred that the forms of two ladies, dressed in white, might be seen pacing up and down. Night after night the people of the neighbourhood used to come and watch them, and curiosity brought many from a great distance. The figures were always to be seen at dusk; they walked arm-in-arm over precisely the same spot of ground till morning light. Mr Wilkie adds that, about twelve years before the time of his noting down the story, while some workmen were repairing the road, they took up the large flat stones upon which foot-passengers crossed the burn, and found beneath them the skeletons of two women lying side by side. After this discovery, the Bow-brig ladies were never again seen to walk in the Three-corner-field.

Mr Wilkie says further, that he received this account from a gentleman who saw and examined the skeletons, and who added that they were believed to be those of two ladies, sisters to a former laird of Littledean. Their brother is said to have killed them in a fit of passion, because they interfered to protect from ill-usage a young lady whom he had met at Bow-brig-syke. He placed their bodies upon the bridge, and lowered the flat stones upon them to prevent discovery. Some years later he met with his own death near the same fatal spot. While riding with his dogs he fell over the brae opposite to the bridge, and was found lying dead by the Tweed side. Tradition identifies him with the Laird Harry Gilles, whose adventure in hunting has already been related.

*W. Henderson, *Folk-Lore of the Northern Counties*.

THE ISLAND CAVE*

More than a couple of hundred years ago, 'Dhonnocha Reamhar', or 'Stout Duncan', a near kinsman to M'Donald of Glengarry, immured and confined his wife, a daughter of M'Donald, Lord of the Isles, within a cave on an island in Loch Chon. The lady, who was both young and beautiful, had brought him, through their union, large tracts of land in the shires of Argyle and Ross. 'Dhonnocha Reamhar', who was then well advanced in years, and who had led a lawless life all his days, appropriated the prize greedily. Resembling in character Rob Roy, or Robin Hood, he considered nothing to become him ill, and various charges of hame-sucken[1] and cattle-lifting were brought against him. Of a wild and roving disposition, he would never remain at rest, but was continually engaged in fighting, plundering, and robbing the neighbouring clans. Once, when hotly pursued by a party of M'Phersons in Rannoch, he came to the river Erichty, and finding it in full spate,[2] swollen with recent rains, gave himself up for lost. Nevertheless, he started afresh, and, nothing daunted, ran down the river's edge until he reached a bend in the stream, where it takes a sharp and sudden turn. On either side were steep rocks, rising perpendicular from the water, and about sixteen feet apart. Between the rocks the water rushed with great velocity, throwing the foam and spray high into the air. 'Dhonnocha Reamhar' quailed before the means of escape, but was resolved at all hazards to make a desperate

*Mr Kennedy's MS.
[1] A law term denoting an assault committed within the house of the person assaulted.
[2] Flood.

attempt for freedom. Rather than fall into the hands of the enemy, he determined there and then to leap into the roaring torrent, and so end for ever his warfare. Taking a run of a few yards, and leaping high into the air, he cleared the chasm, and landed safe on the opposite side. Having thus obtained a footing, he turned round upon his pursuers, defied them, and laughed them to scorn. Enraged beyond measure, the baffled enemy retired in disgust.

Shortly after this event his marriage took place. It proved a very unhappy one. Growing tired of the society of his wife, he resolved to get rid of her at once and for ever. Having chosen the island cave of Loch Chon as a fit place to perpetrate his awful and bloodthirsty deed, he succeeded, by wiles and other means known only to himself, in inducing his wife to accompany him in an expedition to the loch. On their arrival, he persuaded her to enter the cave, where, without a word of warning, he suddenly overpowered her and left her to perish. On his way out he blocked up the mouth of the cavern with stones, and, fearful lest the deed should be discovered, obliterated all traces of footprints in and around the cave's mouth. The island is only about fifteen yards from the shore of the lake, and is thickly studded with trees. All traces of the cave are now lost; but it is supposed to lie towards the west end, where the ground is very rocky. Times without number have I endeavoured to ascertain its whereabouts, but have always failed to discover it. Tradition declares that the lady was never seen again alive; but to this day her wraith is said to haunt the lonely shores of Loch Chon.

'Dhonnocha Reamhar's Leap' is about a mile and a half from Loch Chon, and about a quarter of a mile west from the junction of the Ault-na-Chon burn with the river

Erichty. The rocks on either side of the stream, where he performed his remarkable feat, are now well worn with the inroads of the river; but they are still, as of old, lofty and dangerous.

THE SPECTRE PIPER*

During the rebellion of 1745–6, in Prince Charles Edward Stuart's retreat from Derby, the main body of his Highlanders were compelled, on their northward march through Badenoch, to make a short halt in the wild pass of Drumouchtdar, in order to enable the rear and other stragglers of the ill-fated army to overtake them. Being sorely harassed by a party of English cavalry, the men began to murmur and grumble at the Prince's stubbornness in not giving them permission to dislodge the horsemen, and at his seeming unwillingness to give the order to charge.

The unfortunate Prince, not wishing to risk a combat with the fresh and well-trained dragoons, owing to the deplorable condition of his own men, endeavoured to reason them out of such an insane idea, and explained to the best of his ability the utter foolishness of the strategic move in question. But the eager Highlanders paid no attention to his counsel, and determined on their own account to assail the enemy. Resolving at all hazards to dislodge them from the position they occupied on the hill, they straightway prepared for action, and about midday marched to the attack. The assaulting party consisted of two regiments of infantry – the clans M'Donald and M'Pherson; while the enemy mustered about six hundred men.

*Mr Kennedy's MS.

The battle commenced, and great was the carnage, as the dismounted cavalry, in expectation of an attack, had during the night constructed earthworks and dug trenches. Every available stone and boulder had in this way been piled up to repel the onslaught of the fierce Gaels, who charged with terrible force, hewing and slashing everything that came in their way, and destroying all and sundry who impeded their progress. Savage and grim, they were determined either to conquer or die; and, charging again and again, they at last with difficulty gained a footing within the trenches. Once there, the dirk and claymore soon decided the fortune of the day, and eventually the enemy, completely routed, fled in all directions. Hamstringing the horses, the Celts immediately started in pursuit, and cut down the fugitives to a man. The last man of the English who met his death at the point of a Highland claymore fell on the banks of the 'Ault-na-Sassenach', or 'Englishman's burn'. The burn is called by that name to this day; and the spot where the last survivor was killed is marked by an upright stone erected in the moss, about nine yards from the edge of the stream.

And it is said that persons who chance to pass over the moor at the hour of gloaming are suddenly startled by the wailing of a bagpipe, but find it impossible to tell from whence comes the melancholy strain. People also aver that, in the twilight, other sounds no less strange and weird are heard, and that spectres are seen engaged in mortal combat on the site of the old battle-ground. Various antique relics – claymores, dirks, musket-barrels, and the like – have been found in and about the trenches, a few of which I have myself seen.

PRINCE CHARLIE'S CAVE*

On the summit of Meilchan, about three hundred yards off the main road between Rannoch and Dalnacardoch, is to be found a cave, where the bonnie but unfortunate Prince Charles Edward Stuart is said to have lurked previous to his enibarkation for France. After the terrible massacre on Culloden (locally better known by the name of Drumossie) Moor, he wandered through the Highlands like a hare before the hounds. Pursued by the terrible sleuth-hounds of the Duke of Cumberland, he experienced many hair's-breadth escapes, and was several times on the point of being captured. But it is unnecessary for me here to dwell upon the unlucky prince's many adventures. Enough to say that, hard pressed and hunted as he was, he succeeded in eluding his enemies, and the following year escaped to France. Over the length and breadth of Scotland the name of 'Bonnie Prince Charlie' is a household word; and over all Albyn his fame is handed down in song and in story.

Prince Charlie's cave is situated on the summit of a small green hillock, and is composed of solid limestone rock. It is rather a difficult and hazardous matter to obtain access to it, the mouth of the cavern being flooded with water, and the arched entrance exceedingly low.

So far as I understand, the cave has never yet been explored, although its exploration has several times been attempted; the last occasion being about twelve or fourteen years ago.

A young gentleman, a member of a shooting-party, then volunteered to enter it; and, with that object in view, started to creep on hands and knees into the cavern.

His exit was more rapid than his entrance, and he made

*Mr Kennedy's MS.

his reappearance before his companions, pale and trembling. On being asked what he had heard or seen, he declared that he had beheld, crouching at the further end of the cave, the figure of a tall, lean man, dressed in the Highland garb; who had appeared to threaten him should he offer to penetrate further into the cavern.

Tradition says the cave possesses more than one entrance – the other being away in the direction of Loch Chon. Situated as it is, on mossy and treacherous ground, very few people trouble to visit the spot, notwithstanding the amount of interest which clings to it.

ADAM BELL*

This tale, which may be depended on as in every part true, is singular, from the circumstance of its being insolvable, either from the facts that have been discovered relating to it, or by reason; for though events sometimes occur among mankind, which at the time seem inexplicable, yet there being always some individuals acquainted with the primary causes of these events, they seldom fail of being brought to light before all the actors in them, or their confidants, are removed from this state of existence. But the causes which produced the events here related have never been accounted for in this world; even conjecture is left to wander in a labyrinth, unable to get hold of the thread that leads to the catastrophe.

Mr. Bell was a gentleman of Annandale, in Dumfriesshire, in the south of Scotland, and proprietor of a considerable estate in that district, part of which he occupied himself. He lost his father when he was an infant,

*James Hogg, *The Ettrick Shepherd's Tales*.

and his mother, dying when he was about twenty years of age, left him the sole proprietor of the estate, besides a large sum of money at interest, for which he was indebted, in a great measure, to his mother's parsimony during his minority. His person was tall, comely, and athletic, and his whole delight was in warlike and violent exercises. He was the best horseman and marksman in the county, and valued himself particularly upon his skill in the broadsword. Of this he often boasted aloud, and regretted that there was not one in the county whose skill was in some degree equal to his own.

In the autumn of 1745, after being for several days busily and silently employed in preparing for his journey, he left his own house, and went to Edinburgh, giving at the same time such directions to his servants as indicated his intention of being absent for some time.

A few days after he had left his home, one morning, while his housekeeper was putting the house in order for the day, her master, as she thought, entered by the kitchen door, the other being bolted, and passed her in the middle of the floor. He was buttoned in his greatcoat, which was the same he had on when he went from home; he likewise had the same hat on his head, and the same whip in his hand which he took with him. At sight of him she uttered a shriek, but recovering her surprise, instantly said to him, 'You have not stayed so long from us, Sir.' He made no reply, but went sullenly into his own room, without throwing off his greatcoat. After a pause of about five minutes, she followed him into the room. He was standing at his desk with his back towards her. She asked him if he wished to have a fire kindled, and afterwards if he was well enough; but he still made no reply to any of these questions. She was astonished, and returned into the kitchen. After tarrying about other five minutes, he went out at the front door, it being then open, and walked deliberately towards the bank of the river Kinnel, which was deep and wooded, and in that he vanished from her sight. The woman ran out in the utmost consternation to acquaint the men who were servants belonging to the house; and coming to one of the ploughmen, she told him that their master was come home, and had certainly lost his reason, for that he was wandering about the house and would not speak. The man loosed his horses from the plough and came home, listened to the woman's relation, made her repeat it again and again, and then assured her that she was raving, for their master's horse was not in the stable, and of course he could not be come home. However, as she persisted in her asseveration with every appearance of sincerity, he went into the linn to see what was become of his mysterious master. He was neither to be seen nor heard of in all the country. It was then concluded that the housekeeper had seen an apparition, and that something had befallen their master; but on consulting with some old people, skilled in these matters, they learned that when a 'wraith', or apparition of a living person, appeared while the sun was up, instead of being a prelude of instant death, it prognosticated very long life; and, moreover, that it could not possibly be a ghost that she had seen, for they always chose the night season for making their visits. In short, though it was the general topic of conversation among the servants and the people in the vicinity, no reasonable conclusion could be formed on the subject.

The most probable conjecture was that as Mr Bell was known to be so fond of arms, and had left his home on the very day that Prince Charles Stuart and his Highlanders defeated General Hawley on Falkirk Muir, he had gone either with him or the Duke of Cumberland to the north. It was, however, afterwards ascertained that he had never joined any of the armies. Week passed after week, and month after month, but no word of Mr Bell. A female cousin was his nearest living relation; her husband took the management of his affairs; and concluding that he had either joined the army, or drowned himself in the Kinnel, when he was seen go into the linn, made no more inquiries after him.

About this very time, a respectable farmer, whose surname was M'Millan, and who resided in the neighbourhood of Musselburgh, happened to be in Edinburgh about some business. In the evening he called upon a friend who lived near Holyrood House; and being seized with an indisposition, they persuaded him to tarry with them all night. About the middle of the night he grew exceedingly ill, and not being able to find any rest or ease in his bed, imagined he would be the better of a walk. He put on his clothes, and, that he might not disturb the family, slipped quietly out at the back door, and walked in St Anthony's garden behind the house. The moon shone so bright, that it was almost as light as noonday, and he had scarcely taken a single turn, when he saw a tall man enter from the other side, buttoned in a drab-coloured greatcoat. It so happened that at that time M'Millan, stood in the shadow of the wall, and perceiving that the stranger did not observe him, a thought struck him that it would not be amiss to keep himself concealed, that he might see what the man was going to be about. He walked backwards and forwards for some time in apparent impatience, looking at his watch every minute, until at length another man came in by the same way, buttoned likewise in a greatcoat, and having a bonnet on his head. He was remarkably stout made, but considerably lower in stature than the other. They exchanged only a single word; then turning both about, they threw off their coats, drew their swords, and began a most desperate and well-contested combat.

The tall gentleman appeared to have the advantage. He constantly gained ground on the other, and drove him half round the division of the garden in which they fought. Each of them strove to fight with his back towards the moon, so that it might shine full in the face of his opponent; and many rapid wheels were made for the purpose of gaining this position. The engagement was long and obstinate, and by the desperate thrusts that were frequently aimed on both sides, it was evident that they meant one another's destruction. They came at length within a few yards of the place where M'Millan still stood concealed. They were both out of breath, and at that instant a small cloud chancing to overshadow the moon, one of them called out, 'Hold, we cannot see.' They uncovered their heads, wiped their faces, and as soon as the moon emerged from the cloud, each resumed his guard. Surely that was an awful pause! And short, indeed, was the stage between it and eternity with the one! The tall gentleman made a lounge at the other, who parried and returned it; and as the former sprung back to avoid the thrust, his foot slipped, and he stumbled forward towards his antagonist, who dextrously met his breast in the fall with the point of his sword, and ran him through the body. He made only one feeble convulsive struggle, as if attempting to rise, and expired almost instantaneously.

M'Millan was petrified with horror; but conceiving himself to be in a perilous situation, having stolen out of the house at that dead hour of the night, he had so much presence of mind as to hold his peace, and to keep from interfering in the smallest degree.

The surviving combatant wiped his sword with great composure; put on his bonnet, covered the body with one of the greatcoats, took up the other, and departed. M'Millan returned quietly to his chamber without awakening any of the family. His pains were gone, but his mind was shocked and exceedingly perturbed; and after deliberating until morning, he determined to say nothing of the matter, and to make no living creature acquainted with what he had seen, thinking that suspicion would infallibly rest on him. Accordingly, he kept his bed next morning, until his friend brought him the tidings that a gentleman had been murdered at the back of the house during the night. He then arose and examined the body, which was that of a young man, seemingly from the country, having brown hair, and fine manly features. He had neither letter, book, nor signature of any kind about him that could in the least lead to a discovery of who he was; only a common silver watch was found in his pocket, and an elegant sword was clasped in his cold bloody hand, which had an A. and B. engraved on the hilt. The sword had entered at his breast, and gone out at his back a little below the left shoulder. He had likewise received a slight wound on the sword arm.

The body was carried to the dead-room, where it lay for eight days, and though great numbers inspected it, yet none knew who or whence the deceased was, and he was at length buried among the strangers in Greyfriars Churchyard.

Sixteen years elapsed before M'Millan mentioned to any person the circumstance of his having seen the duel, but at that period, being in Annandale receiving some sheep that he had bought, and chancing to hear of the astonishing circumstances of Bell's disappearance, he divulged the whole. The time, the description of his person, his clothes, and, above all, the sword with the initials of his name engraved upon it, confirmed the fact beyond the smallest shadow of doubt that it was Mr Bell whom he had seen killed in the duel behind the Abbey. But who the person was that slew him, how the quarrel commenced, or who it was that appeared to his housekeeper, remains to this day a profound secret, and is likely to remain so, until that day when every deed of darkness shall be brought to light.

Some have even ventured to blame M'Millan for the whole, on account of his long concealment of facts, and likewise in consideration of his uncommon bodily strength and daring disposition, he being one of the boldest and most enterprising men of the age in which he lived; but all who knew him despised such insinuations, and declared them to be entirely inconsistent with his character, which was most honourable and disinterested; and besides, his tale has every appearance of truth.

THE THURSO MERCHANT'S WRAITH*

Richard Sinclair, a merchant in the town of Thurso, returning home one evening with his servant, as they came to the river close by the town, found it was swelled by a fall of rain, and much increased by the tide, which was in. The latter seemed averse to ford, which his master observing, alighted and gave him his own horse, and mounted his servant's horse, with which, having entered the river, he was soon carried by the flood out of his saddle, and was drowned. His wife, knowing nothing then of the matter, as

*Rev. John Frazer, Δευτεροσκοπια, or a Brief Discourse concerning the Second Sight, commonly so called. (Seventeenth century.)

she was going from one room to another in her own house, saw Mr Sinclair go up the stair to his own room, and called to a servant-maid to bring him a candle and make up a fire; but after the servant had brought the light in great haste, found no person within. In less than an hour the noise went through the town that the gentleman was drowned.

BURIED TREASURE DISCOVERED*

Kenneth Morrison, of good repute with his contemporaries, then living at Glendale, had a revelation in a dream, as follows: A person informed him in sleep, that if he should repair to the kirk of Killchoan, and look out at the east window, he might see at the distance of two pair of butts, in a direct line eastward, a stone larger than any near it in that direction; upon removing of which he would find silver, which had been hid under it. And accordingly he lost no time, but went the next day to take his observation as he was directed, and having found out the stone, was not disappointed, as there was under it a heap of silver of different sizes, coinage and value; a part of which was not then of the common currency.

A WEDDING FRUSTRATED†

A young girl was contracted to a gentleman in the Lewis, equal to her in birth and other circumstances; yet a seer that lived about the family frequently told her she should never be married to that man; and even upon the night when the

*From the same.
†From the same.

parson came to the place to join their hands, the bride and bridegroom being completely dressed, and ready waiting to fulfil the ceremony, the seer persisted in what he had so often asserted. In the meantime, the bride having stepped out of the room after night fell, she was met with by a gentleman, at the head of twelve persons, who carried her to a boat hard by, and conducted her to an island at some distance from the continent, waited there until they were married, and the seer's prediction fulfilled.

THE STRAW-ROPE GARTERS*

Barbara M'Pherson, relict of the deceased Mr Alexander M'Leod, late minister of St Kilda, informed me the natives of that island have a particular kind of the second-sight, which is always a fore-runner of their approaching end. Some months before they sicken they are haunted with an apparition resembling themselves in all respects as to their person, features, or clothing. This image (seemingly animated) walks with them in the fields in broad daylight; and if they are employed in delving, harrowing, seed-sowing, or any other occupation, they are at the same time mimicked by this ghostly visitant. My informer added further, that having visited a sick person, one of the inhabitants, she had the curiosity to inquire of him if at any time he had seen any resemblance of himself as above described? He answered in the affirmative, and told her that, to make further trial, as he was going out of his house on a morning, he put on straw-rope garters, instead of those he formerly used, and

*From the same.

having gone to the fields, his other self appeared in such garters. The conclusion was, the sick man died of that ailment, and she no longer questioned the truth of those remarkable presages.

THE WHINGER*

A noble peer of this nation being one morning in his bed-chamber, and attended by several persons, when his servant had put a new coat upon his Lord, a gentleman standing by presently cried out, 'For God's sake, my Lord, put off that coat'; and being asked the reason, he replied that he saw a whinger, or poignard, stick in the breast of it. The noble peer, esteeming this as a mere fancy, replied, 'This coat is honestly come by, and I see no reason why I may not wear it.' The gentleman still entreated, and earnestly craved that it might be put off: upon which debate, the noble peer's lady being not far off, came in, and being informed of the whole affair, entreated her Lord to comply with the gentleman's desire, which he did; meantime one of the servants standing by desired the lady to give it him, and he would wear it. She granted his request, who put it on; and ere night he was stabbed by a poignard, in that very place which the gentleman had pointed to in the morning.

*From the same.

THE HERRING-CURER'S VISION*

In the year 1665, Alexander Wood, eldest son to the Laird of Nether Benholm, in Angus, having ended his apprentice-ship with a merchant in Edinburgh, told Mr James Walker that (in the year 1662 or 1663) he had been employed by his master to go to the Lewis to make up herring; and being there, and having a good tack of herring, their salt and casks were all made use of and then they being idle, he began to fret that his master had delayed so long to supply them; and being one day drinking in a country house, and complaining, he went to the door of the house, and there followed him a countryman, who said to him, 'If you will give me a small hire, I'll tell you what has become of the ship you are looking for;' and without more ado he set his foot upon the gentleman's foot, in which time he saw the ship in a great storm, ready to perish, and the seamen casting out their lading to lighten the ship; but when the countryman's foot was off he saw nothing. The ship at that time was about 100 miles from them, and about 48 hours thereafter she came into the same harbour, and had been in the same condition he saw her in at that time the coun-tryman's foot was on his foot.

THE WINDING SHEET†

I was resolved to pay a visit to an English gentleman, Sir William Sacheverill, who had a commission from the English Court of Admiralty to give his best trial to find out gold or money, or any other thing of note, in one of the

*From the same.
†From the same.

ships of the Spanish Armada, that was blown up in the bay of Topper-Mory, in the Sound of Mull. And having condescended upon the number of men that were to go with me, one of the number was a handsome boy that waited upon my own person; and, about an hour before I made sail, a woman, that was also one of my own servants, spoke to one of the seamen, and bade him to dissuade me to take that boy along with me, or if I did I should not bring him back alive; the seaman answered, he had not confidence to tell me such unwarrantable trifles. I took my voyage, and sailed the length of Topper-Mory; and having stayed two or three nights with that liberal and ingenuous gentleman, who himself had collected many observations of the Second Sight in the Isle of Man, and compared his notes and mine together, I then took leave of him. In the meantime my boy grew sick of a vehement bloody flux – the winds turned cross, that I could neither sail nor row – the boy died with me the eleventh night from his decumbiture. The next morning the wind made fair, and the seaman to whom the matter was foretold related the whole story when he saw it verified. I carried the boy's corpse aboard with me, and after my arrival, and his burial, I called suddenly for the woman, and asked her what warrant she had to foretell the boy's death. She said that she had no other warrant but that she saw, two days before I took my voyage, the boy walking with me in the fields, sewed up in his winding sheets from top to toe, and that she had never seen this in others but she found that they shortly thereafter died; and therefore concluded that he would die too, and that shortly.

APPARITION OF A CORPSE*

Donald M'Kinnon, an honest man, residing in Glendale, informed me that when living in South Uist he had a servant woman remarkable for the second-sight; who, upon a night as she was grinding at the quirn,[1] saw a corpse, stretched to a loose deal in the partition, in his winding sheet, which only came down to his knees. This she immediately told publicly to all that were present. She had the same representation twice or thrice thereafter, which made the wife of the house apprehensive it concerned herself or some of her children. In a short time thereafter one John M'Kinnon, a neighbouring tenant, sickened, of which he soon died. John Oag M'Kinnon, brother to the defunct, who had the charge to provide for his interment, applied to the declarant for timber to make his coffin, who gave him the deal to which the said seer had seen a corpse stretched at four different times. And as they could get no linen for a winding sheet, the said John Oag was obliged to make use of one of his own wearing shirts, which, when it was put on the corpse, reached but to his knees, thereby fulfilling the second-sight in all its circumstances.

PHANTOM FUNERALS†

There was a singular instance of the second-sight seen at Groul, in Mininish. The possessor then of that tack, on a fair day, took a walk in the fields for his recreation, and as he was a man advanced in years, and being somewhat tired

*From the same.
†From the same.
[1]Hand-mill.

with his exercise, reposed himself on the banks of a rivulet close to the common road, which afforded him an agreeable prospect. Soon after he had sat down, he observed a person coming that way who had been his acquaintance, and whom he invited to rest, as he had done, in that agreeable solitude. In a little time his companion discovered himself to be a seer of the second-sight, by informing Groul that a small company, with a corpse on a bier, were just then coming the way that leads from Breattle to the churchyard, which was in their sight, and about to cross the river that runs through the glen; and that, at the same time, he perceived a numerous gathering coming in at the other end of the glen, from Harport; which the first gathering having also observed (as he thought), laid down the bier, and made the best of their way to join the multitude, whom they followed until they came opposite to the place where they left the bier, to which they returned with a supply of men to help them; upon which both the corpses were carried with ease to the churchyard and interred. In some short time thereafter, Groul saw from his own house two gatherings with corpses coming the different roads, and in the same circumstances as already described.

THE DEATH PORTENT*

A farmer's wife, who resided on the banks of the Ale, near St Boswells', looking out at window, thought she saw a funeral approaching; and at once mentioned the circumstance to some neighbours, then with her in the house. They ran out to look, but came back and sat down again, saying she must be mistaken, for there was nothing of the

*W. Henderson, *Folk-Lore of the Northern Counties.*

kind to be seen. The woman felt restless, however, and out of spirits; she could not help going to the window again, and again she saw the funeral moving on. Her friends ran out of doors and looked along the road, but still could perceive nothing; a third time she went to the window, and exclaimed, 'It is fast coming on, and will soon be at the door.' No other person could discern anything; but within half-an-hour a confused noise was heard outside, and the farm-servants entered, bearing her husband's lifeless body. He had died suddenly, by a fall from his cart.

COMIC TALES

Comic Tales

THE WEE BUNNOCK*

'Some tell about their sweethearts, how they tirled them to
  the winnock,[1]
But I'll tell you a bonny tale about a guid aitmeal
  bunnock.'

There lived an auld man and an auld wife at the side o' a
burn. They had twa kye, five hens and a cock, a cat and twa
kittlins. The auld man lookit after the kye, and the auld
wife span on the tow-rock.[2] The kittlins aft grippit at the
auld wife's spindle, as it tussled owre the hearth-stane.
'Sho, sho,' she wad say; 'gae wa',' and so it tussled
about.

Ae day, after parritch-time, she thought she would ha'e a
bunnock. Sae she bakit twa aitmeal bunnocks, and set them
to the fire to harden. After a while, the auld man came in,

*Chambers, *Popular Rhymes of Scotland.*
[1]Tapped at the window to bring them out.
[2]Spinning-wheel.

and sat down aside the fire, and takes ane o' the bunnocks, and snappit it through the middle. When the tither ane sees this, it rins aff as fast as it could, and the auld wife after't, wi' the spindle in the tae hand and the tow-rock in the tither. But the wee bunnock wan awa', and out o' sight, and ran till it came to a guid muckle thack house,[1] and ben[2] it ran boldly to the fireside; and there were three tailors sitting on a muckle table. When they saw the wee bunnock come ben, they jumpit up, and gat in ahint the guidwife, that was cardin' tow about the fire. 'Hout,' quo' she, 'be na fleyt;[3] it's but a wee bunnock. Grip it, and I'll gie ye a soup milk till't.' Up she gets wi' the tow-cards, and the tailor wi' the goose, and the twa 'prentices, the ane wi' the muckle shears, and the tither wi the lawbrod;[4] but it jinkit[5] them, and ran round about the fire; and ane o' the 'prentices, thinking to snap it wi' the shears, fell i' the ase-pit. The tailor cuist[6] the goose, and the guidwife the tow-cards; but a' wadna do. The bunnock wan awa', and ran till it came to a wee house at the roadside; and in it rins, and there was a weaver sittin' on the loom, and the wife winnin' a clue o' yarn.

'Tibby,' quo' he, 'what's tat?' 'Oh,' quo' she, 'it's a wee bunnock.' 'It's weel come,' quo' he, 'for our sowens[7] were but thin the day. Grip it, my woman; grip it.' 'Ay,' quo' she; 'what recks! That's a clever bunnock. Kep,[8] Willie; kep, man.' 'Hout,' quo' Willie; 'cast the clue at it.' But the bunnock whipit round about, and but the

---

[1]Good big thatched house.   [5]Dodged.
[2]In.   [6]Cast.
[3]Frightened.   [7]Pottage.
[4]Ironing-board.   [8]Catch.

floor,[1] and aff it gaed, and owre the knowe,[2] like a new-tarred sheep or a daft yell cow.[3] And forrit it runs to the neist house, and ben to the fireside. And there was the guidwife kirnin'.[4] 'Come awa', wee bunnock,' quo' she; 'I'se hae ream[5] and bread the day.' But the wee bunnock whipit round about the kirn, and the wife after't, and i' the hurry she had near-hand coupit the kirn.[6] And afore she got it set right again, the wee bunnock was aff, and down the brae to the mill. And in it ran.

The miller was siftin' meal i' the trough; but, looking up, 'Ay,' quo' he, 'it's a sign o' plenty when ye're rinnin' about, and naebody to look after ye. But I like a bunnock and cheese. Come your wa's ben, and I'll gie ye a night's quarters.' But the bunnock wadna trust itsel' wi' the miller and his cheese. Sae it turned and ran its wa's out; but the miller didna fash his head wi't.[7] So it toddled awa', and ran till it came to the smithy. And in it rins, and up to the studdy.[8] The smith was making horsenails. Quo' he, 'I like a bicker o' guid yill[9] and a weel-toastit bunnock. Come your wa's in by here.' But the bunnock was frightened when it heard about the yill, and turned and aff as hard as it could, and the smith after't, and cuist the hammer. But it whirlt awa', and out o' sight in a crack, and ran till it came to a farm-house wi' a guid muckle peat- stack at the end o't. Ben it rins to the fireside. The guidman was clovin' lint,[10] and the guidwife hecklin'.[11] 'Oh, Janet,' quo' he, 'there's a wee bunnock; I'se ha'e the hauf o't.' 'Weel, John, I'se ha'e the tither hauf. Hit it owre the back wi' the clove.' But the bunnock playt jink-about.[12]

---

[1] Toward the door.
[2] Knoll.
[3] A cow that has ceased to give milk.
[4] Churning.
[5] Cream.
[6] Overturned the churn.
[7] Didn't trouble his head about it.
[8] Anvil.
[9] A stoup of good ale.
[10] Separating lint from the stalk.
[11] Dressing flax.
[12] 'Catch me if you can.'

'Hout tout,' quo' the wife, and gart the heckle flee at it.[1]
But it was owre clever for her.

And aff and up the burn it ran to the neist house, and
whirlt its wa's ben to the fireside. The guidwife was stirrin'
the sowens, and the guidman plettin' spret-binnings for the
kye.[2] 'Ho, Jock,' quo' the guidwife, 'come here. Thou's
aye crying about a wee bunnock. Here's ane. Come in,
haste ye, and I'll help thee to grip it.' 'Ay, mither, whaur
is't?' 'See there. Rin owre o' that side.' But the bunnock
ran in ahint the guidman's chair. Jock fell among the
sprits. The guidman cuist a binning, and the guidwife the
spurtle.[3] But it was owre clever for Jock and her baith. It
was aff and out o' sight in a crack, and through among the
whins,[4] and down the road to the neist house, and in, and
ben to the fireside. The folk were just sittin' down to their
sowens, and the guidwife scartin' the pat.[5] 'Losh,' quo'
she, 'there's a wee bunnock come in to warm itsel' at
our fireside.' 'Steek[6] the door,' quo' the guidman, 'and
we'll try to get a grip o't.' When the bunnock heard that,
it ran but the house, and they after't wi' their spunes, and
the guidman cuist his bunnat.[7] But it whirlt awa', and ran,
and better ran, till it came to another house. And when it
gaed ben, the folk were just gaun to their beds. The
guidman was castin' aff his breeks, and the guidwife
rakin' the fire. 'What's tat?' quo' he. 'Oh,' quo' she,
'it's a wee bunnock.' Quo' he, 'I could eat the hauf o't, for
a' the brose I hae suppit.' 'Grip it,' quo' the wife, 'and I'll
hae a bit too.' 'Cast your breeks at it – kep – kep!' The
guidman cuist the breeks, and had near-hand smoor't[8] it.

---

[1] Let fly the comb at it.
[2] Plaiting straw-ropes for the cows.
[3] Stick used for stirring porridge.
[4] Furze.
[5] Scraping the pot.
[6] Fasten.
[7] Bonnet, cap.
[8] Smothered.

But it warsl't[1] out, and ran, and the guidman after't, wanting the breeks. And there was a clean chase owre the craft[2] park, and up the wunyerd, and in amang the whins. And the guidman lost it, and had to come his wa's trottin' hame hauf nakit. But now it was grown dark, and the wee bunnock couldna see; but it gaed into the side o' a muckle whin bush, and into a tod's hole.[3] The tod had gotten nae meat for twa days. 'Oh, welcome, welcome,' quo' the tod, and snappit it in twa i' the middle. And that was the end o' the wee bunnock.

> 'Now, be ye lords or commoners,
> Ye needna laugh nor sneer,
> For ye'll be a' i' the tod's hole
> In less than a hunner year.'

THE TALE OF THE SHIFTY LAD, THE WIDOW'S SON*

I

There was at some time or other before now a widow, and she had one son. She gave him good schooling, and she was wishful that he should choose a trade for himself; but he said he would not go to learn any art, but that he would be a thief.

His mother said to him: 'If that is the art that thou art going to choose for thine ownself, thine end is to be hanged at the bridge of Baile Cliabh,[4] in Eirinn.'

---

[1]Struggled.   [3]A fox's hole.
[2]Croft.   [4]Dublin.
*Campbell, *Popular Tales of the West Highlands*.

But it was no matter, he would not go to any art, but to be a thief; and his mother was always making a prophecy to him that the end of him would be, hanging at the Bridge of Baile Cliabh, in Eirinn.

On a day of the days, the widow was going to the church to hear the sermon, and was asking the Shifty Lad, her son, to go with her, and that he should give over his bad courses; but he would not go with her; but he said to her: 'The first art of which thou hearest mention, after thou hast come out of the sermon, is the art to which I will go afterwards.'

She went to the church full of good courage, hoping that she would hear some good thing.

He went away, and he went to a tuft of wood that was near to the church; and he went in hiding in a place where he could see his mother when she should come out of the church; and as soon as she came out he shouted, 'Thievery! thievery! thievery!' She looked about, but she could not make out whence the voice was coming, and she went home. He ran by the way of the short cut, and he was at the house before her, and he was seated within beside the fire when she came home. He asked her what tale she had got; and she said that she had not got any tale at all, but that 'thievery, thievery, thievery, was the first speech she heard when she came out of the church.'

He said 'That was the art that he would have.'

And she said, as she was accustomed to say: 'Thine ending is to be hanged at the bridge of Baile Cliabh, in Eirinn.'

On the next day, his mother herself thought that, as nothing at all would do for her son but that he should be a thief, she would try to find him a good aid-to-learning; and she went to the black gallows bird of Aachaloinne, a very cunning thief who was in that place; and though they had knowledge that he was given to stealing, they were not finding any way for catching him. The widow asked the Black Rogue if he would take her son to teach him roguery. The Black Rogue said, 'If he were a clever lad that he would take him, and if there were a way of making a thief of him that he could do it;' and a covenant was made between the Black Rogue and the Shifty Lad.

When the Shifty Lad, the widow's son, was making ready for going to the Black Rogue, his mother was giving him counsel, and she said to him: 'It is against my will that thou art going to thievery; and I was telling thee, that the end of thee is to be hanged at the bridge of Baile Cliabh, Eirinn;' but the Shifty Lad went home to the Black Rogue.

The Black Rogue was giving the Shifty Lad every knowledge he might for doing thievery; he used to tell him about the cunning things that he must do, to get a chance to steal a thing; and when the Black Rogue thought that the Shifty Lad was good enough at learning to be taken out with him, he used to take him out with him to do stealing; and on a day of these days the Black Rogue said to his lad –

'We are long enough thus, we must go and do something. There is a rich tenant near to us, and he has much money in his chest. It was he who bought all that there was of cattle to be sold in the country, and he took them to the fair, and he sold them; he has got the money in his chest, and this is the time to be at him, before the people are paid for their lot of cattle; and unless we go to seek the money at this very hour, when it is gathered together, we shall not get the same chance again.'

The Shifty Lad was as willing as himself; they went away to the house, they got in at the coming on of the night, and they went up upon the loft,[1] and they went in hiding up

[1]The loft meant is the space in the roof of a cottage which is above the rafters, and is used as a kind of store.

there; and it was the night of SAMHAIN (Halloween); and there assembled many people within to keep the Savain hearty as they used to do. They sat together, and they were singing songs, and at fun burning the nuts, and at merry-making.

The Shifty Lad was wearying that the company was not scattering; he got up and he went down to the byre, and he loosed the bands off the necks of the cattle, and he returned and he went up upon the loft again. The cattle began goring each other in the byre, and roaring. All that were in the room ran to keep the cattle from each other till they could be tied again; and in the time while they were doing this, the Shifty Lad went down to the room and he stole the nuts with him, and he went up upon the loft again, and he lay down at the back of the Black Rogue.

There was a great leathern hide at the back of the Black Rogue, and the Shifty Lad had a needle and thread, and he sewed the skirt of the Black Rogue's coat to the leathern hide that was at his back; and when the people of the house came back to the dwelling-room again, their nuts were away; and they were seeking their nuts; and they thought that it was some one who had come in to play them a trick that had taken away their nuts, and they sat down at the side of the fire quietly and silently.

Said the Shifty Lad to the Black Rogue, 'I will crack a nut.'

'Thou shalt not crack one,' said the Black Rogue; 'they will hear thee, and we shall be caught.'

Said the Shifty Lad, 'I never yet was a Savain night without cracking a nut,' and he cracked one.

Those who were seated in the dwelling-room heard him, and they said –

'There is some one up on the loft cracking our nuts; we will go and catch them.'

When the Black Rogue heard that, he sprang off the loft and he ran out, and the hide dragging at the tail of his coat. Every one of them shouted that there was the Black Rogue stealing the hide with him. The Black Rogue fled, and the people of the house after him; and he was a great distance from the house before he got the hide torn from him, and was able to leave them. But in the time that the people of the house were running after the Black Rogue, the Shifty Lad came down off the loft; he went up about the house, he hit upon the chest where the gold and the silver was; he opened the chest, and he took out of it the bags in which the gold and silver was, that was in the chest; and he took with him a load of the bread, and of the butter, and of the cheese, and of everything that was better than another which he found within; and he was gone before the people of the house came back from chasing the Black Rogue.

When the Black Rogue reached his home, and he had nothing, his wife said to him, 'How hast thou failed this journey?'

Then the Black Rogue told his own tale; and he was in great fury at the Shifty Lad, and swearing that he would serve him out when he got a chance at him.

At the end of a little while after that, the Shifty Lad came in with a load upon him.

Said the wife of the Black Rogue, 'But I fancy that thou art the better thief!'

The Black Rogue said not a word till the Shifty Lad showed the bags that he had full of gold and silver; then said the Black Rogue, 'But it is thou that wert the smart lad!'

They made two halves of the gold and silver, and the Black Rogue got the one half, and the Shifty Lad the other half. When the Black Rogue's wife saw the share that came to them, she said, 'Thou thyself art the worthy thief!' and she had more respect for him after that than she had for the Black Rogue himself.

II

The Black Rogue and the Shifty Lad went on stealing till they had got much money, and they thought that they had better buy a drove of cattle, and go to the fair with it to sell, and that people would think that it was at drovering they had made the money that they had got. The two went, and they bought a great drove of cattle, and they went to a fair that was far on the way from them. They sold the drove, and they got the money for them, and they went away to go home. When they were on the way, they saw a gallows on the top of a hill, and the Shifty Lad said to the Black Rogue, 'Come up till we see the gallows; some say that the gallows is the end for the thieves at all events.'

They went up where the gallows was, and they were looking all about it. Said the Shifty Lad, 'Might we not try what kind of death is in the gallows, that we may know what is before us, if we should be caught at roguery. I will try it myself first.'

The Shifty Lad put the cord about his own neck, and he said to the Black Rogue, 'Here, draw me up, and when I am tired above I will shake my legs, and then do thou let me down.'

The Black Rogue drew the cord, and he raised the Shifty Lad aloft off the earth, and at the end of a little blink the Shifty Lad shook his legs, and the Black Rogue let him down.

The Shifty Lad took the cord off his neck, and he said to

the Black Rogue, 'Thou thyself hast not ever tried anything that is so funny as hanging. If thou wouldst try once, thou wouldst have no more fear for hanging. I was shaking my legs for delight, and thou wouldst shake thy legs for delight too if thou wert aloft.'

Said the Black Rogue, 'I will try it too, so that I may know what it is like.'

'Do,' said the Shifty Lad; 'and when thou art tired above, whistle and I will let thee down.'

The Black Rogue put the cord about his neck, and the Shifty Lad drew him up aloft; and when the Shifty Lad found that the Black Rogue was aloft against the gallows, he said to him, 'Now, when thou wantest to come down, whistle, and if thou art well pleased where thou art, shake thy legs.'

When the Black Rogue was a little blink above, he began to shake his legs and to kick; and the Shifty Lad would say, 'Oh! art thou not funny! art thou not funny! art thou not funny! When it seems to thee that thou art long enough above, whistle.'

But the Black Rogue has not whistled yet. The Shifty Lad tied the cord to the lower end of the tree of the gallows till the Black Rogue was dead; then he went where he was, and he took the money out of his pouch, and he said to him, 'Now, since thou hast no longer any use for this money, I will take care of it for thee.' And he went away, and he left the Black Rogue hanging there. Then he went home where was the house of the Black Rogue, and his wife asked where was his master?

The Shifty Lad said, 'I left him where he was, upraised above the earth.'

The wife of the Black Rogue asked and asked him about her man, till at last he told her; but he said to her, that he would marry her himself. When she heard that, she cried that the Shifty Lad had killed his master, and he was nothing but a thief. When the Shifty Lad heard that he fled. The chase was set after him; but he found means to go in hiding in a cave, and the chase went past him. He was in the cave all night, and the next day he went another way, and he found means to fly to Eirinn.

III

He reached the house of a wright, and he cried at the door, 'Let me in.'

'Who art thou?' said the wright.

'I am a good wright, if thou hast need of such,' said the Shifty Lad.

The wright opened the door, and he let in the Shifty Lad, and the Shifty Lad began to work at carpentering along with the wright.

When the Shifty Lad was a day or two in their house, he gave a glance thither and a glance hither about the house, and he said, 'O choin! what a poor house you have, and the king's store-house so near you.'

'What of that?' said the wright.

'It is,' said the Shifty Lad, 'that you might get plenty from the king's store-house if you yourselves were smart enough.'

The wright and his wife would say, 'They would put us in prison if we should begin at the like of that.'

The Shifty Lad was always saying that they ought to break into the king's store-house, and they would find plenty in it; but the wright would not go with him; but the Shifty Lad took with him some of the tools of the wright, and he went himself and he broke into the king's store-house, and he took with him a load of the butter and of the cheese of the king, and he took it to the house of the wright. The things pleased the wife of the wright well, and she was willing that her own husband should go there the next night. The wright himself went with his lad the next night, and they got into the store-house of the king, and they took with them great loads of each thing that pleased them best of all that was within in the king's store-house.

But the king's people missed the butter and the cheese and the other things that had been taken out of the store-house, and they told the king how it had happened.

The king took the counsel of the Seanagal about the best way of catching the thieves, und the counsel that the Seanagal gave them was that they should set a hogshead of soft pitch under the hole where they were coming in. That was done, and the next night the Shifty Lad and his master went to break into the king's store-house.

The Shifty Lad put his master in before him, and the master went down into the soft pitch to his very middle, and he could not get out again. The Shifty Lad went down, and he put a foot on each of his master's shoulders, and he put out two loads of the king's butter and of the cheese at the hole; and at the last time when he was coming out, he swept the head off his master, and he took the head with him, and he left the trunk in the hogshead of pitch, and he went home with the butter and with the cheese, and he took home the head, and he buried it in the garden.

When the king's people went into the store-house, they found a body without a head into the hogshead of pitch; but they could not make out who it was. They tried if they could find any one at all that could know him by the clothes, but his clothes were covered with pitch so that they could not make him out. The king asked the counsel of the Seanagal about it; and the counsel that the Seanagal gave was, that they should set the trunk aloft on the points of the spears of the soldiers; to be carried from town to town, to see if they could find any one at all that would take sorrow for it; or to try if they could hear any one that would make a painful cry when they should see it; or if they should not see one that should seem about to make a painful cry when the soldiers should be going past with it. The body was taken out of the hogshead of pitch, and set on the points of the spears; and the soldiers were bearing it aloft on the points of their long wooden spears, and they were going from town to town with it; and when they were going past the house of the wright, the wright's wife made a tortured scream, and swift the Shifty Lad cut himself with the adze; and he kept saying to the wright's wife, 'The cut is not as bad as thou thinkest.'

The commander-in-chief, and his lot of soldiers, came in and they asked,

'What ailed the housewife?'

Said the Shifty Lad, 'It is that I have just cut my foot with the adze, and she is afraid of blood;' and he would say to the wife of the wright, 'Do not be so much afraid; it will heal sooner than thou thinkest.'

The soldiers thought that the Shifty Lad was the wright, and that the wife whom they had seen was the wife of the Shifty Lad; and they went out, and they went from town to town; but they found no one besides, but the wife of the wright herself, that made cry or scream when they were coming past her.

They took the body home to the king's house; and the king took another counsel from his Seanagal, and that was to hang the body to a tree in an open place, and soldiers to watch it that none should take it away, and the soldiers to be looking if any should come the way that should take pity or grief for it.

The Shifty Lad came past them, and he saw them; he went and he got a horse, and he put a keg of whisky on each side of the horse in a sack, and he went past the soldiers with it, as though he were hiding from them. The soldiers thought that it was so, or that he had taken something which he ought not to have; and some of them ran after him, and they caught the old horse and the whisky; but the Shifty Lad fled, and he left the horse and the whisky with them. The soldiers took the horse and the kegs of whisky back to where the body was hanging against the mast. They looked what was in the kegs; and when they understood that it was whisky that was in them, they got a drinking cup, and they began drinking until at last every one of them was drunk, and they lay and they slept. When the Shifty Lad saw that, that the soldiers were laid down and asleep and drunk, he returned and took the body off the mast. He set it crosswise on the horse's back, and he took it home; then he went and he buried the body in the garden where the head was.

When the soldiers awoke out of their sleep, the body was stolen away; they had nothing for it but to go and tell it to the king. Then the king took the counsel of the Seanagal; and the Seanagal said to them, all that were in his presence, that his counsel to them was, to take out a great black pig that was there, and that they should go with her from town to town; and when they should come to any place where the body was buried, that she would root it up.

They went and they got the black pig, and they were going from farm to farm with her, trying if they could find out where the body was buried. They went from house to house with her, till at last they came to the house where the Shifty Lad and the wright's widow were dwelling. When they arrived they let the pig loose about the grounds. The Shifty Lad said that he himself was sure that thirst and hunger was on them; that they had better go into the house and that they should get meat and drink; and that they should let their weariness from off them, in the time when the pig should be seeking about his place.

They went in, and the Shifty Lad asked the wright's widow that she should set meat and drink before the men. The widow of the wright set meat and drink on the board, and she set it before them; and in the time while they were eating their meat, the Shifty Lad went out to see after the pig; and the pig had just hit upon the body in the garden; and the Shifty Lad went and he got a great knife and he cut the head off her, and he buried herself and her head beside the body of the wright in the garden.

When those who had the care of the pig came out, the pig was not to be seen. They asked the Shifty Lad if he had seen her; he said that he had seen her, that her head was up and she was looking upwards, and going two or three steps now and again; and they went with great haste to the side where the Shifty Lad said the pig had gone.

When the Shifty Lad found that they had gone out of sight, he set everything in such a way that they should not hit upon the pig. They on whom the care of the pig was laid went and they sought her every way that it was likely she might be. Then when they could not find her, they had nothing for it but to go to the king's house and tell how it had happened.

Then the counsel of the Seanagal was taken again; and the counsel that the Seanagal gave them was, that they should set their soldiers out about the country at free quarters; and at whatsoever place they should get pig's flesh, or in whatsoever place they should see pig's flesh, unless those people could show how they had got the pig's flesh that they might have, that those were the people who killed the pig, and that had done every evil that had been done.

The counsel of the Seanagal was taken, and the soldiers sent out to free quarters about the country; and there was a band of them in the house of the wright's widow where the Shifty Lad was. The wright's widow gave their supper to the soldiers, and some of the pig's flesh was made ready for them; and the soldiers were eating the pig's flesh, and praising it exceedingly. The Shifty Lad understood what was the matter, but he did not let on.[1] The soldiers were set to lie out in the barn; and when they were asleep the Shifty Lad went out and he killed them. Then he went as fast as he could from house to house, where the soldiers were at free quarters, and he set the rumour afloat amongst the people of the houses, that the soldiers had been sent out about the country to rise in the night and kill the people in their beds; and he found means to make the people of the country believe him, so that the people of each house killed all the soldiers that were asleep in their barns; and when the soldiers did not come home at the time they should, some went to see what had happened to them; and when they arrived, it was so that they found the soldiers dead in the barns where they had been asleep; and the people of each house denied that they knew how the soldiers had been put to death, or who had done it.

The people who were at the ransacking for the soldiers went to the king's house, and they told how it had happened; then the king sent word for the Seanagal to get

[1]Divulge.

counsel from him; the Seanagal came, and the king told
how it had happened, and the king asked counsel from him.
This is the counsel that the Seanagal gave the king, that he
should make a feast and a ball, and invite the people of the
country; and if the man who did the evil should be there,
that he was the man who would be the boldest who would
be there, and that he would ask the king's daughter herself
to dance with him. The people were asked to the feast and
the dance; and amongst the rest the Shifty Lad was asked.
The people came to the feast, and amongst the rest came
the Shifty Lad. When the feast was past, the dance began;
and the Shifty Lad went and he asked the king's daughter
to dance with him; and the Seanagal had a vial full of black
stuff, and the Seanagal put a black dot of the stuff that was
in the vial on the Shifty Lad. But it seemed to the king's
daughter that her hair was not well enough in order, and
she went to a side chamber to put it right; and the Shifty
Lad went in with her; and when she looked in the glass, he
also looked in it, and he saw the black dot that the Seanagal
had put upon him. When they had danced till the tune of
music was finished, the Shifty Lad went and he got a chance
to steal the vial of the Seanagal from him unknown to him,
and he put two black dots on the Seanagal, and one black
dot on twenty other men besides, and he put the vial back
again where he found it.

Between that and the end of another while, the Shifty
Lad came again and he asked the king's daughter to dance.
The king's daughter had a vial also, and she put a black dot
on the face of the Shifty Lad; but the Shifty Lad got the vial
whipped out of her pocket, unknown to her; and since
there were two black dots on him, he put two dots on
twenty other men in the company, and four black dots on
the Seanagal. Then when the dancing was over, some were

sent to see who was the man on whom were the two black dots. When they looked amongst the pepple, they found twenty men on whom there were two black dots, and there were four black dots on the Seanagal; and the Shifty Lad found means to go swiftly where the king's daughter was, and to slip the vial back again into her pocket. The Seanagal looked and he had his black vial; the king's daughter looked and she had her own vial; then the Seanagal and the king took counsel; and the last counsel that they made was that the king should come to the company, and say, that the man who had done every trick that had been done must be exceedingly clever; if he would come forward and give himself up, that he should get the king's daughter to marry, and the one half of the kingdom while the king was alive, and the whole of the kingdom after the king's death. And every one of those who had the two black dots on their faces came and they said that it was they who had done every cleverness that had been done. Then the king and his high council went to try how the matter should be settled; and the matter which they settled was, that all the men who had the two black dots on their faces should be put together in a chamber, and they were to get a child, and the king's daughter was to give an apple to the child, and the child was to be put in where the men with the two black dots on their faces were seated, and to whatsoever one the child should give the apple, that was the one who was to get the king's daughter.

That was done, and when the child went into the chamber in which the men were, the Shifty Lad had a shaving and a drone, and the child went and gave him the apple. Then the shaving and the drone were taken from the Shifty Lad, and he was seated in another place, and the apple was given to the child again; and he was taken out of the chamber, and sent in again to see to whom he would give the apple; and since the Shifty Lad had the shaving and the drone before, the child went where he was again, and he gave him the apple. Then the Shifty Lad got the king's daughter to marry.

And shortly after that the king's daughter and the Shifty Lad were taking a walk to Baile Cliabh; and when they were going over the bridge of Baile Cliabh, the Shifty Lad asked the king's daughter what was the name of that place; and the king's daughter told him that it was the bridge of Baile Cliabh, in Eirinn; and the Shifty Lad said –

'Well, then, many is the time that my mother said to me, that my end would be to be hanged at the bridge of Baile Cliabh, in Eirinn; and she made me that prophecy many a time when I might play her a trick.'

And the king's daughter said, 'Well, then, if thou thyself shouldst choose to hang over the little side wall of the bridge, I will hold thee aloft a little space with my pocket napkin.'

And they were at talk and fun about it; but at last it seemed to the Shifty Lad that he would do it for sport, and the king's daughter took out her pocket napkin, and the Shifty Lad went over the bridge, and he hung by the pocket napkin of the king's daughter as she let it over the little side wall of the bridge, and they were laughing to each other.

But the king's daughter heard a cry, 'The king's castle is going on fire!' and she started, and she lost her hold of the napkin; and the Shifty Lad fell down, and his head struck against a stone, and the brain went out of him; and there was in the cry but the sport of children; and the king's daughter was obliged to go home a widow.

LOTHIAN TOM*

I

Tom being grown up to years and age of man, thought himself wiser and slyer than his father: and there were several things about the house which he liked better than to work; so he turned to be a dealer amongst brutes, a cowper of horses and cows, etc., and even wet ware, amongst the brewers and brandy shops, until he cowped himself to the toom[1] halter, and then his parents would supply him no more. He knew his grandmother had plenty of money, but she would give him none; but the old woman had a good black cow of her own, which Tom went to the fields one evening and catches, and takes her to an old waste house which stood at a distance from any other, and there he kept her two or three days, giving her meat and drink at night when it was dark, and made the old woman believe somebody had stolen the cow for their winter's mart, which was grief enough to the old woman, for the loss of her cow. However, she employs Tom to go to a fair that was near by, and buy her another; she gives him three pounds, which Tom accepts of very thankfully, and promises to buy her one as like the other as possibly he could get; then he takes a piece of chalk, and brays it as small as meal, and steeps it in a little water, and therewith rubs over the cow's face and back, which made her baith brucket and rigget.[2] So Tom in the morning takes the cow to a public-house within a little of the fair, and left her till the fair was over, and then drives her home before him; and as soon as they came home, the

---

*Dougal Graham, *The Comical Tricks of Lothian Tom*.
[1]Empty.
[2]Spotted on body and face.

cow began to rout as it used to do, which made the old woman to rejoice, thinking it was her own cow; but when she saw her white, sighed and said, 'Alas! thou'll never be like the kindly brute my Black Lady, and yet ye rout as like her as ony ever I did hear.' But says Tom to himself, ''Tis a mercy you know not what she says; or all would be wrong yet.' So in two or three days the old woman put forth her bra' rigget cow in the morning with the rest of her neighbours' cattle, but it came on a sore day of heavy rain, which washed away all the white from her face and back; so the old woman's Black Lady came home at night, and her rigget cow went away with the shower, and was never heard of. But Tom's father having some suspicion, and looking narrowly into the cow's face, found some of the chalk not washed away, and then he gave poor Tom a hearty beating, and sent him away to seek his fortune with a skin full of sore bones.

II

Tom being now turned to his own shifts, considered with himself how to raise a little more money; and so gets a string as near as he could guess to be the length of his mother, and to Edinburgh he goes, to a wright who was acquainted with his father and mother. The wright asked him how he did; he answered him, very soberly, he had lost a good dutiful mother last night, and there's a measure for the coffin. Tom went out and stayed for some time, and then comes in again, and tells the wright he did not know what to do, for his father had ordered him to get money from such a man, whom he named, and he that day was gone out of town . . . The wright asked him how much he wanted. To which he answered, a guinea and a half. Then Tom gave him strict orders to be out next day against eleven o'clock with the coffin, and he should get his money altogether. So Tom set off to an ale-house with the money, and lived well while it lasted. Next morning the wright and his two lads went out with the coffin; and as they were going into the house they met Tom's mother, who asked the master how he did, and where he was going with that fine coffin? Not knowing well what to say, being surprised to see her alive, at last he told her that her son brought in the measure the day before, and had got a guinea and a half from him, with which he said he was to buy some necessaries for the funeral. 'Oh, the rogue !' said she, 'has he play'd me that?' So the wright got his lent money, and so much for his trouble, and had to take back his coffin with him again.

III

Tom being short of money, began to think how he could raise a fresh supply; so he went to the port among the shearers,[1] and there he hired about thirty of them, and agreed to give them a whole week's shearing at tenpence a-day, which was twopence higher than any had got that year; this made the poor shearers think he was a very honest, generous, and genteel master, as ever they met with for he took them all into an ale-house, and gave them a hearty breakfast. 'Now,' says Tom, 'when there is so many of you together, and perhaps from very different parts, and being unacquainted with one another, I do not know but there may be some of you honest men and some

[1]Reapers.

of you rogues; and as you are all to lie in one barn together, any of you who has got money, you will be surest to give it to me, and I'll mark it down in my book with your names, and what I receive from each of you, and you shall have it all again on Saturday night, when you receive your wages.' 'Oh, very well, goodman, there's mine; take mine,' said every one faster than another. Some gave him five, six, seven, and eight shillings – even all that they had earn'd thro' the harvest, which amounted to near seven pounds sterling. So Tom, having got all their money, he goes on with them till about three miles out of town, and coming to a field of standing corn, though somewhat green, yet convenient for his purpose, as it lay at some distance from any house – so he made them begin work there, telling them he was going to order dinner for them, and send his own servants to join them. Then he sets off with all the speed he could, but takes another road into the town lest they should follow and catch him. Now when the people to whom the corn belonged saw such a band in their field, they could not understand the meaning of it: so the farmer whose corn it was went off, crying always as he ran to them to stop; but they would not, until he began to strike at them, and they at him, he being in a great passion, as the corn was not fully ripe. At last, by force of argument, and other people coming up to them, the poor shearers were convinced they had got the bite, which caused them to go away sore lamenting their misfortune.

Two or three days thereafter, as Tom was going down Canongate in Edinburgh, he meets one of his shearers, who knew and kept fast by him, demanding back his money, and also satisfaction for the rest. 'Whisht, whisht,' says

Tom, 'and you'll get yours and something else beside.' So Tom takes him into the gaol, and calls for a bottle of ale and a dram, then takes the gaoler aside, as if he had been going to borrow some money from him, and says to the gaoler, 'This man is a great thief. I and other two have been in search of him these three days, and the other two men have the warrant with them; so if you keep this rogue here till I run and bring them, you shall have a guinea in reward.' 'Yes,' says the gaoler, 'go, and I'll secure the rogue for you.' So Tom got off; leaving the poor innocent fellow and the gaoler struggling together, and then sets out for England directly.

IV

Tom having now left his own native country, went into the county of Northumberland, where he hired himself to an old miser of a farmer, where he continued for several years, performing his duty in his service very well, though sometimes playing tricks on those about him. But his master had a naughty custom, he would allow them no candle at night, to see with when at supper. So Tom one night sets himself next his master, and as they were all about to fall on, Tom puts his spoon into the heart of the dish, where the crowdy was hottest, and claps a spoonful into his master's mouth. 'A pox on you for a rogue,' cried his master, 'for my mouth is all burnt.' 'A pox on you for a master,' says Tom, 'for you keep a house as dark as Purgatory, for I was going to my mouth with the soup and missed the way, it being so dark. Don't think, master, that I am such a big fool as to feed you while I have a mouth of my own.' So from that night that Tom burnt his master's mouth with the hot crowdy, they always got a candle to show them light at supper, for his master would feed no more in the dark while Tom was present

There was a servant girl in the house, who always when she made the beds neglected to make Tom's, and would have him do it himself. 'Well, then,' says Tom, 'I have harder work to do, and I shall do that too.' So next day when Tom was at the plough, he saw his master coming from the house towards him. He left the horses and the plough standing in the field, and goes away towards his master, who cried, 'What is wrong? or is there anything broke with you?' 'No, no,' said Tom; 'but I am going home to make my bed; it has not been made these two weeks, and now it is about the time the maid makes all the rest, so I'll go and make mine too.' 'No, no,' says his master, 'go to your plough, and I'll cause it to be made every night.' 'Then,' says Tom, 'I'll plough two or three furrows more in the time.' So Tom gained his end.

V

One day a butcher came and bought a fine fat calf from Tom's master, and Tom laid it on the horse's neck, before the butcher. When he was gone, 'Now,' says Tom, 'what will you hold, master, but I'll steal the calf from the butcher before he goes two miles off?' Says his master, 'I'll hold a guinea you don't.' 'Done,' says Tom. Into the house he goes, and takes a good shoe of his master's, and runs another way across a field, till he got before the butcher, near the corner of a hedge, where there was an open and turning of the way; here Tom places himself behind the hedge, and throws the shoe into the middle of the highway; so, when the butcher came up riding, with his calf before him, 'Hey,' said he to himself, 'there's a good shoe! if I knew how to get on my calf again, I would light for it; but what signifies one shoe without its neighbour?' So on he rides and lets it lie. Tom then slips out and takes up the shoe, and runs across the fields until he got before the butcher, at another open of a hedge, about half-a-mile distant, and throws out the shoe again on the middle of the road; then up comes the butcher, and seeing it, says to himself: 'Now I shall have a pair of good shoes for the lifting;' and down he comes, lays the calf on the ground, and tying his horse to the hedge, runs back thinking to get the other shoe, in which time Tom whips up the calf and shoe, and home he comes demanding his wager, which his master could not refuse, being so fairly won. The poor butcher not finding the shoe, came back to his horse, and missing the calf, knew not what to do; but thinking it had broke the rope from about its feet, and had run into the fields, the butcher spent the day in search of it amongst the hedges and ditches, and returned to Tom's master's at night, intending to go in search again for it next day, and gave them a tedious relation how he came to lose it by a cursed pair of shoes, which he believed the devil had dropped in his way and taken the calf and shoes along with him, but he was thankful he had left his old horse to carry him home. Next morning Tom set to work, and makes a fine white face on the calf with chalk and water; then brings it out and sells it to the butcher, which was good diversion to his master and other servants, to see the butcher buy his own calf again. No sooner was he gone with it, but Tom says, 'Now, master, what will you hold but I'll steal it from him again ere he goes two miles off?' 'No, no,' says his master, 'I'll hold no more bets with you; but I'll give you a shilling if you do it.' 'Done,' says Tom, 'it shall cost you no more;' and away he runs through the fields, until he came before the butcher, hard by the place where he stole the calf from him the day before and there he lies down behind the hedge, and as the butcher came past, he put his hand on his mouth and cries baw, baw, like a calf. The butcher hearing this, swears to himself that there was the calf he had lost the day before: down he comes, and throws the calf on the ground, gets through the hedge in all haste, thinking he had no more to do but to take it up; but as he came in at one part of the hedge, Tom jumped out at another, and gets the calf on his back; then goes over the hedge on the other side, and through the fields he came safely home, with the calf on his back, while the poor butcher spent his time and labour in vain, running from hedge to hedge, and hole to hole, seeking the calf. So the butcher returning to his horse again, and finding his other calf gone, he concluded that it was done by some invisible spirit about that spot of ground, and so went home lamenting the loss of his calf. When Tom got home he washed the white face off the stolen calf, and his master sent the butcher word to come and buy another calf, which he accordingly did in a few days after, and Tom sold him the same calf a third time, and then told him the whole affair as it was acted, giving him his money again. So the butcher got fun for his trouble.

THE PLOUGHMAN'S GLORY; OR, TOM'S SONG

As I was a-walking one morning in the spring,
I heard a young ploughman so sweetly to sing,
And as he was singing these words he did say,
No life is like the ploughman's in the month of May.

The lark in the morning rises from her nest,
And mounts in the air with the dew on her breast,
And with the jolly ploughman she'll whistle and she'll sing,
And at night she'll return to her nest back again.

If you walk in the fields any pleasure to find,
You may see what the ploughman enjoys in his mind;
There the corn he sows grows and the flowers do spring,
And the ploughman's as happy as a prince or a king.

When his day's work is done that he has to do,
Perhaps to some country walk he will go;
There with a sweet lass he will dance and sing,
And at night return with his lass back again.

Then he rises next morning to follow his team,
Like a jolly ploughman so neat and so trim;
If he kiss a pretty girl he will make her his wife,
And she loves her jolly ploughman as dear as her life.

There's Molly and Dolly, Nelly and Sue;
There's Ralph, John, and Willie, and young Tommy too;
Each lad takes his lass to the wake or the fair,
Adzooks! they look rarely I vow and declare.

THE WITTY EXPLOITS OF MR. GEORGE
BUCHANAN, THE KING'S FOOL*

I

Mr George Buchanan was a Scotsman born, and though of mean parentage, made great progress in learning. As for his understanding and ready wit, he excelled all men then alive in the age that ever proposed questions to him. He was servant or teacher to King James the Sixth, and one of his private counsellors, but publicly acted as his fool.

George happened one time to be in company with a bishop, and so they fell to dispute anent education, and he blanked the bishop remarkably, and the bishop himself owned he was worsted. Then one of the company addressed himself to him in these words: 'Thou, Scot,' said he, 'should not have left thy country.' 'For what?' says he. 'Because thou hast carried all the wisdom that is in it hither with thee.' 'No, no,' says he; 'the shepherds in Scotland will dispute with any bishop in London, and exceed them very far in education.' The bishops then took this as an affront, and several noblemen affirmed it to be as the Scot had said: bets were laid on each side, and three of the bishops were chosen, and sent away to Scotland to dispute it with the shepherds, accompanied with several others, who were to bear witness of what they should hear pass between them. Now George, knowing which way they went, immediately took another road and was in Scotland before them. He then made an acquaintance with a shepherd on the border, whose pasture lay on the wayside where the bishops were to pass; and there he mounted himself in shepherd's dress; and when he saw the bishops

*John Cheap the Chapman's Library. By Dougal Graham (?).

appear, he conveyed his flock to the roadside, and fell a-chanting at a Latin ballad. When the bishops came up to George, one of them asked him in French what o'clock it was? To which he answered in Hebrew, 'It is directly about the time of day it was yesterday at this time.' Another asked him, in Greek, what countryman he was? To which he answered in Flemish, 'If ye knew that, you would be as wise as myself.' A third asked him, in Dutch 'Where were you educated?' To which he answered, in Earse, 'Herding my sheep between this and Lochaber.' This they desired him to explain into English, which he immediately did. 'Now,' said they one to another, 'we need not proceed any farther.' 'What,' says George, 'are you butchers? I'll sell you a few sheep.' To this they made no answer, but went away shamefully, and said they believed the Scots had been through all the nations in the world for their education, or the devil had taught them. Now, when George had ended this dispute with the bishops, he stripped off his shepherd's dress, and up through England he goes, with all the haste imaginable, so that he arrived at the place from whence they set out three days before the judges, and went every day asking if they were come, so that he might not be suspected. As soon as they arrived, all that were concerned in the dispute, and many more, came crowding in, to hear what news from the Scottish shepherds, and to know what was done. No sooner had the three gentlemen declared what had passed between the bishops and the shepherds, whom they found on the Scots border, but the old bishop made answer, 'And think you,' said he, 'that a shepherd could answer these questions? It has been none else but the devil; for the Scots ministers themselves could not do it; they are but ignorant of such matters, a parcel of beardless boys.' Then George thought it was time to take speech in hand. 'Well, my lord bishop,' says George, 'you call them a parcel of ignorant, beardless boys. You have a great long beard yourself, my lord bishop, and if grace were measured by beards, you bishops and the goats would have it all, and that would be quite averse to Scripture.' 'What,' says the bishop, 'are you a Scot?' 'Yes,' says George, 'I am a Scot.' 'Well,' says the bishop, 'and what is the difference between a Scot and a sot?' 'Nothing at present,' says George, 'but the breadth of the table' – there being a table betwixt the bishop and George. So the bishop went off in a high passion, while the whole multitude were like to split their jaws with laughter.

II

One night a Highland drover chanced to have a drinking bout with an English captain of a ship, and at last they came to be very hearty over their cups, so that they called in their servants to have a share of their liquor. The drover's servant looked like a wild man, going without breeches, stockings, or shoes, not so much as a bonnet on his head, with a long peeled rung in his hand. The captain asked the drover how long it was since he catched him? He answered, 'It is about two years since I hauled him out of the sea with a net, and afterwards ran into the mountains, where I catched him with a pack of hounds.' The captain believed it was so. 'But,' says he, 'I have a servant, the best swimmer in the world.' 'Oh, but,' says the drover, 'my servant will swim him to death.' 'No, he will not,' says the captain; 'I'll lay two hundred crowns on it.' 'Then,' says the drover, 'I'll hold it one to one,' and staked directly, the day being appointed when trial was to be made. Now the

drover, when he came to himself, thinking on what a
bargain he had made, did not know what to do, knowing
very well that his servant could swim none. He, hearing of
George being in town, who was always a good friend to
Scotsmen, went unto him and told him the whole story, and
that he would be entirely broke, and durst never return
home to his own country, for he was sure to lose it. Then
George called the drover and his man aside, and instructed
them how to hehave, so that they should be safe and gain
too. So accordingly they met at the place appointed. The
captain's man stripped directly and threw himself into the
sea, taking a turn until the Highlandman was ready, for the
drover took some time to put his servant in order. After he
was stripped, his master took his plaid, and rolled a
kebbuck of cheese, a big loaf, and a bottle of gin in it, and
this he bound on his shoulder, giving him directions to tell
his wife and children that he was well, and to be sure he
returned with an answer against that day se'nnight. As he
went into the sea, he looked back to his master, and called
out to him for his claymore. 'And what waits he for now?'
says the captain's servant. 'He wants his sword,' says his
master. 'His sword,' says the fellow; 'what is he to do with
a sword?' 'Why,' says his master, 'if he meets a whale or a
monstrous beast, it is to defend his life; I know he will have
to fight his way through the north seas, ere he get to
Lochaber.' 'Then,' cried the captain's servant, 'I'll swim
none with him, if he take his sword.' 'Ay, but,' says his
master, 'you shall, or lose the wager; take you another
sword with you.' 'No,' says the fellow; 'I never did swim
with a sword, nor any man else, that ever I saw or heard of.
I know not but that wild man will kill me in the deep water;
I would not for the whole world venture myself with him
and a sword.' The captain seeing his servant afraid to

venture, or if he did he would never see him again alive, therefore desired an agreement with the drover, who at first seemed unwilling; but the captain putting it in his will, the drover quit him for half the sum. This he came to through George's advice.

III

George was met one day by three bishops, who paid him the following compliments: Says the first, 'Good-morrow, Father Abraham'; says the second, 'Good-morrow, Father Isaac'; says the third, 'Good-morrow, Father Jacob.' To which he replied, 'I am neither Father Abraham, Father Isaac, nor Father Jacob , but I am Saul, the son of Kish, sent out to seek my father's asses, and, lo! I have found three of them.' Which answer fully convinced the bishops that they had mistaken their man.

IV

A poor Scotchman dined one day at a public-house in London upon eggs, and not having money to pay, got credit till he should return. The man, being lucky in trade, acquired vast riches; and after some years, happening to pass that way, called at the house where he was owing the dinner of eggs. Having called for the innkeeper, he asked him what he had to pay for the dinner of eggs he got from him such a time. The landlord, seeing him now rich, gave him a bill of several pounds; telling him, as his reason for so extravagant a charge, that these eggs, had they been hatched, would have been chickens; and these laying more eggs, would have been more chickens; and so on, multiplying the eggs and their product, till such time as their value amounted to the sum charged. The man, refusing to comply with this demand, was charged before a judge. He then made his case known to George, his countryman, who promised to appear in the hour of cause, which he accordingly did, all in a sweat, with a great basket of boiled pease, which appearance surprised the judge, who asked him what he meant by these boiled pease? Says George, 'I am going to sow them.' 'When will they grow?' said the judge. 'They will grow,' said George, 'when sodden eggs grow chickens.' Which answer convinced the judge of the extravagance of the innkeeper's demand, and the Scotsman was acquitted for two-pence halfpenny.

V

George was professor of the College of St Andrews, and slipped out one day in his gown and slippers, and went on his travels through Italy and several other foreign countries, and after seven years returned with the same dress he went off in; and, entering the college, took possession of his seat there, but the professor in his room quarrelling him for so doing. 'Ay,' says George, 'it is a very odd thing that a man cannot take a walk out in his slippers, but another will take up his seat.' And so set the other professor about his business.

VI

Two drunken fellows one day fell a-beating one another on the streets of London, which caused a great crowd of people to throng together to see what it was. A tailor being at work up in a garret, about three or four storeys high, and he hearing the noise in the street, looked over the window, but could not well see them. He began to stretch himself, making a long neck, until he fell down out of the window, and alighted on an old man who was walking on the street. The poor tailor was more afraid than hurt, but the man he fell on died directly. His son caused the tailor to be apprehended and tried for the murder of his father. The jury could not bring it in wilful murder, neither could they altogether free the tailor. The jury gave it over to the judges, and the judges to the king. The king asked George's advice on this hard matter. 'Why,' says George, 'I will give you my opinion in a minute: you must cause the tailor to stand in the street where the old gentleman was when he was killed by the tailor, and then let the old gentleman's son, the tailor's adversary, get up to the window from whence the tailor fell, and jump down, and so kill the tailor as he did his father.' The tailor's adversary hearing this sentence passed, would not venture to jump over the window, and so the tailor got clear off.

LITERARY TALES

Literary Tales*

THE HAUNTED SHIPS†

'Alexander Macharg, besides being the laird of three acres
of peatmoss, two kale gardens, and the owner of seven
good milch cows, a pair of horses, and six pet sheep, was
the husband of one of the handsomest women in seven
parishes. Many a lad sighed the day he was brided; and a
Nithsdale laird and two Annandale moorland farmers
drank themselves to their last linen, as well as their last
shilling, through sorrow for her loss. But married was the
dame; and home she was carried, to bear rule over her
home and her husband, as an honest woman should. Now
ye maun ken that, though the flesh-and-blood lovers of
Alexander's bonnie wife all ceased to love and to sue her
after she became another's, there were certain admirers did
not consider their claim at all abated, or their hopes lessened by the kirk's famous obstacle of matrimony. Ye have

*The Editor has adopted this term to denote popular tales, or tales founded
upon popular superstition, which have received a literary clothing.
†Allan Cunningham, *Traditional Tales of the English and Scottish
Peasantry.*

heard how the devout minister of Tinwald had a fair son carried away, and bedded against his liking to an unchristened bride, whom the elves and the fairies provided; ye have heard how the bonnie bride of the drunken laird of Soukitup was stolen by the fairies out at the back window of the bridal chamber, the time the bridegroom was groping his way to the chamber door; and ye have heard – but why need I multiply cases? such things in the ancient days were as common as candlelight. So ye'll no hinder certain water elves and sea fairies, who sometimes keep festival and summer mirth in these old haunted hulks, from falling in love with the weel-faured wife of Laird Macharg; and to their plots and contrivances they went, how they might accomplish to sunder man and wife; and sundering such a man and such a wife was like sundering the green leaf from the summer, or the fragrance from the flower.

'So it fell on a time that Laird Macharg took his half-net on his back, and his steel spear in his hand, and down to Blawhooly Bay gade he, and into the water he went right between the two haunted hulks,[1] and, placing his net, awaited the coming of the tide. The night, ye maun ken, was mirk, and the wind lowne,[2] and the singing of the increasing waters among the shells and the peebles was heard for sundry miles. All at once lights began to glance and twinkle on board the two Haunted Ships from every hole and seam, and presently the sound as of a hatchet employed in squaring timber echoed far and wide. But if the toil of these unearthly workmen amazed the laird, how much more was his amazement increased when a sharp shrill voice called out, "Ho! brother, what are you doing

---

[1] Two ancient wrecked vessels, to which the peasantry of the Solway shore ascribe a sinister character.
[2] Still.

now?" A voice still shriller responded from the other haunted ship, "I'm making a wife to Sandie Macharg!" and a loud quavering laugh, running from ship to ship, and from bank to bank, told the joy they expected from their labour.

'Now the laird, besides being a devout and a God-fearing man, was shrewd and bold; and in plot, and contrivance, and skill in conducting his designs, was fairly an overmatch for any dozen land elves. But the water elves are far more subtle; besides, their haunts and their dwellings being in the great deep, pursuit and detection is hopeless if they succeed in carrying their prey to the waves. But ye shall hear. Home flew the laird – collected his family around the hearth – spoke of the signs and the sins of the times, and talked of mortification and prayer for averting calamity; and finally, taking his father's Bible, brass clasps, black print, and covered with calf-skin, from the shelf, he proceeded without let or stint to perform domestic worship. I should have told ye that he bolted and locked the door, shut up all inlet to the house, threw salt into the fire, and proceeded in every way like a man skilful in guarding against the plots of fairies and fiends. His wife looked on all this with wonder; but she saw something in her husband's looks that hindered her from intruding either question or advice, and a wise woman was she.

'Near the mid hour of the night the rush of a horse's feet was heard, and the sound of a rider leaping from its back, and a heavy knock came to the door, accompanied by a voice, saying, "The cummer drink's[1] hot, and the knave bairn is expected at Laird Laurie's tonight; sae mount, gudewife, and come."

'"Preserve me!" said the wife of Sandie Macharg; "that's

[1] Gossips' drink.

news indeed! who could have thought it? the laird has been heirless for seventeen years! Now Sandie, my man, fetch me my skirt and hood."

'But he laid his arm round his wife's neck, and said, "If all the lairds in Galloway go heirless, over this door threshold shall you not stir tonight; and I have said, and I have sworn it: seek not to know why or wherefore – but, Lord, send us thy blessed mornlight." The wife looked for a moment in her husband's eyes, and desisted from further entreaty.

"But let us send a civil message to the gossips, Sandie; and had nae ye better say I am sair laid with a sudden sickness? though its sinful-like to send the poor messenger a mile agate with a lie in his mouth without a glass of brandy."

'"To such a messenger, and to those who sent him, no apology is needed," said the austere laird, "so let him depart." And the clatter of a horse's hoofs was heard, and the muttered imprecations of its rider on the churlish treatment he had experienced.

'"Now Sandie, my lad," said his wife, laying an arm particularly white and round about his neck as she spoke, "are you not a queer man and a stern? I have been your wedded wife now these three years; and, beside my dower, have brought you three as bonnie bairns as ever smiled aneath a summer sun. O man, you a douce man, and fitter to be an elder than even Willie Greer himself – I have the minister's ain word for't – to put on these hard-hearted looks, and gang waving your arms that way, as if ye said, 'I winna take the counsel of sic a hempie[1] as you.' I'm your ain leal wife, and will and maun have an explanation."

'To all this Sandie Macharg replied, "It is written –

[1]Hussy.

'Wives, obey your husbands'; but we have been stayed in our devotion, so let us pray'; and down he knelt. His wife knelt also, for she was as devout as bonnie; and beside them knelt their household, and all lights were extinguished.

'"Now this beats a",' muttered his wife to herself; "however, I shall be obedient for a time; but if I dinna ken what all this is for before the morn by sunket-time,[1] my tongue is nae langer a tongue, nor my hands worth wearing."

'The voice of her husband in prayer interrupted this mental soliloquy; and ardently did he beseech to be preserved from the wiles of the fiends, and the snares of Satan; "from witches, ghosts, goblins, elves, fairies, spunkies, and water-kelpies; from the spectre shallop of Solway; from spirits visible and invisible; from the Haunted Ships and their unearthly tenants; from maritime spirits that plotted against godly men, and fell in love with their wives" –

'"Nay, but His presence be near us!" said his wife in a low tone of dismay. "God guide my gudeman's wits; I never heard such a prayer from human lips before. But Sandie, my man, Lord's sake, rise: what fearful light is this? – barn, and byre, and stable, maun be in a blaze; and Hawkie and Hurley, Doddie, and Cherrie, and Damson Plum will be smoored with reek, and scorched with flame."

'"And a flood of light, but not so gross as a common fire, which ascended to heaven and filled all the court before the house, amply justified the good wife's suspicions. But, to the terrors of fire, Sandie was as immovable as he was to the imaginary groans of the barren wife of Laird Laurie; and he held his wife, and threatened the weight of his right hand – and it was a heavy one – to all who ventured abroad, or even unbolted the door. The neighing and prancing of

[1] Breakfast-time; any meal-time.

horses, and the bellowing of cows, augmented the horrors of the night; and to any one who only heard the din, it seemed that the whole onstead was in a blaze, and horses and cattle perishing in the flame. All wiles, common or extraordinary, were put in practice to entice or force the honest farmer and his wife to open the door; and when the like success attended every new stratagem, silence for a little while ensued, and a long, loud, and shrilling laugh wound up the dramatic efforts of the night. In the morning, when Laird Macharg went to the door, he found standing against one of the pilasters a piece of black ship oak, rudely fashioned into something like human form, and which skilful people declared would have been clothed with seeming flesh and blood, and palmed upon him by elfin adroitness for his wife, had he admitted his visitants. A synod of wise men and women sat upon the woman of timber, and she was finally ordered to be devoured by fire, and that in the open air. A fire was soon made, and into it the elfin sculpture was tossed from the prongs of two pairs of pitchforks. The blaze that arose was awful to behold; and hissings, and burstings, and loud cracklings, and strange noises, were heard in the midst of the flame; and when the whole sank into ashes, a drinking cup of some precious metal was found; and this cup, fashioned no doubt by elfin skill, but rendered harmless by the purification with fire, the sons and daughters of Sandie Macharg and his wife drink out of to this very day. Bless all bold men, say I, and obedient wives!'

ELPHIN IRVING*
THE FAIRIES' CUPBEARER

The romantic vale of Corriewater, in Annandale, is regarded by the inhabitants, a pastoral and unmingled people, as the last Border refuge of those beautiful and capricious beings, the fairies. Many old people yet living imagine they have had intercourse of good words and good deeds with the 'good folk'; and continue to tell that in the ancient of days the fairies danced on the hill, and revelled in the glen, and showed themselves, like the mysterious children of the deity of old, among the sons and daughters of men. Their visits to the earth were periods of joy and mirth to mankind, rather than of sorrow and apprehension. They played on musical instruments of wonderful sweetness and variety of note, spread unexpected feasts, the supernatural flavour of which overpowered on many occasions the religious scruples of the Presbyterian shepherds, performed wonderful deeds of horsemanship, and marched in midnight processions, when the sound of their elfin minstrelsy charmed youths and maidens into love for their persons and pursuits; and more than one family of Corriewater have the fame of augmenting the numbers of the elfin chivalry. Faces of friends and relatives, long since doomed to the battle-trench or the deep sea, have been recognised by those who dared to gaze on the fairy march. The maid has seen her lost lover and the mother her stolen child; and the courage to plan and achieve their deliverance has been possessed by at least one Border maiden. In the legends of the people of Corrievale there is a singular mixture of elfin and human adventure, and the traditional

*Allan Cunningham, *Traditional Tales of the English and Scottish Peasantry.*

story of the Cupbearer to the Queen of the Fairies appeals alike to our domestic feelings and imagination.

In one of the little green loops, or bends, on the banks of Corriewater, mouldered walls, and a few stunted wild plum-trees and vagrant roses, still point out the site of a cottage and garden. A well of pure spring-water leaps out from an old tree-root before the door; and here the shepherds, shading themselves in summer from the influence of the sun, tell to their children the wild tale of Elphin Irving and his sister Phemie; and, singular as the story seems, it has gained full credence among the people where the scene is laid.

When Elphin Irving and his sister Phemie were in their sixteenth year, for tradition says they were twins, their father was drowned in Corriewater, attempting to save his sheep from a sudden swell, to which all mountain streams are liable; and their mother, on the day of her husband's burial, laid down her head on the pillow, from which, on the seventh day, it was lifted to be dressed for the same grave. The inheritance left to the orphans may be briefly described: seventeen acres of plough and pasture land, seven milk cows, and seven pet sheep (many old people take delight in odd numbers); and to this may be added seven bonnet-pieces of Scottish gold, and a broadsword and spear, which their ancestor had wielded with such strength and courage in the battle of Dryfe Sands, that the minstrel who sang of that deed of arms ranked him only second to the Scotts and Johnstones.

The youth and his sister grew in stature and in beauty. The brent bright brow, the clear blue eye, and frank and blithe deportment of the former gave him some influence among the young women of the valley; while the latter was no less the admiration of the young men, and at fair and dance, and at bridal, happy was he who touched but her hand or received the benediction of her eye. Like all other Scottish beauties, she was the theme of many a song; and while tradition is yet busy with the singular history of her brother, song has taken all the care that rustic minstrelsy can of the gentleness of her spirit and the charms of her person.

But minstrel skill and true love tale seemed to want their usual influence when they sought to win her attention; she was only observed to pay most respect to those youths who were most beloved by her brother; and the same hour that brought these twins to the world seemed to have breathed through them a sweetness and an affection of heart and mind, which nothing could divide. If, like the virgin queen of the immortal poet, she walked 'in maiden meditation fancy free', her brother Elphin seemed alike untouched with the charms of the fairest virgins in Corrie. He ploughed his field, he reaped his grain, he leaped, he ran, and wrestled, and danced, and sang, with more skill and life and grace than all other youths of the district; but he had no twilight and stolen interviews; when all other young men had their loves by their side, he was single, though not unsought, and his joy seemed never perfect save when his sister was near him. If he loved to share his time with her, she loved to share her time with him alone, or with the beasts of the field, or the birds of the air. She watched her little flock late, and she tended it early; not for the sordid love of the fleece, unless it was to make mantles for her brother, but with the look of one who had joy in its company. The very wild creatures, the deer and the hares, seldom sought to shun her approach, and the bird forsook not its nest, nor stinted its song, when she drew nigh; such is the confidence which maiden innocence and beauty inspire.

It happened one summer, about three years after they

became orphans, that rain had been for awhile withheld from the earth, the hillsides began to parch, the grass in the vales to wither, and the stream of Corrie was diminished between its banks to the size of an ordinary rill. The shepherds drove their flocks to moorlands, and marsh and tarn had their reeds invaded by the scythe to supply the cattle with food. The sheep of his sister were Elphin's constant care; he drove them to the moistest pastures during the day, and he often watched them at midnight, when flocks, tempted by the sweet dewy grass, are known to browze eagerly, that he might guard them from the fox, and lead them to the choicest herbage. In these nocturnal watchings he sometimes drove his little flock over the water of Corrie, for the fords were hardly ankle-deep; or permitted his sheep to cool themselves in the stream, and taste the grass which grew along the brink. All this time not a drop of rain fell, nor did a cloud appear in the sky.

One evening, during her brother's absence with the flock, Phemie sat at her cottage door, listening to the bleatings of the distant folds and the lessened murmur of the water of Corrie, now scarcely audible beyond its banks. Her eyes, weary with watching along the accustomed line of road for the return of Elphin, were turned on the pool beside her, in which the stars were glimmering fitful and faint. As she looked she imagined the water grew brighter and brighter; a wild illumination presently shone upon the pool, and leaped from bank to bank, and suddenly changing into a human form, ascended the margin, and, passing her, glided swiftly into the cottage. The visionary form was so like her brother in shape and air, that, starting up, she flew into the house, with the hope of finding him in his customary seat. She found him not, and, impressed with the terror which a wraith or apparition seldom fails to inspire, she uttered a shriek so loud and so piercing as to be heard at Johnstone Bank, on the other side of the vale of Corrie.

It is hardly known how long Phemie Irving continued in a state of insensibility. The morning was far advanced, when a neighbouring maiden found her seated in an old chair, as white as monumental marble; her hair, about which she had always been solicitous, loosened from its curls, and hanging disordered over her neck and bosom, her hands and forehead. The maiden touched the one, and kissed the other; they were as cold as snow; and her eyes, wide open, were fixed on her brother's empty chair, with the intensity of gaze of one who had witnessed the appearance of a spirit. She seemed insensible of any one's presence, and sat fixed and still and motionless. The maiden, alarmed at her looks, thus addressed her: 'Phemie, lass, Phemie Irving! Dear me, but this be awful! I have come to tell ye that seven of your pet sheep have escaped drowning in the water; for Corrie, sae quiet and sae gentle yestreen, is rolling and dashing frae bank to bank this morning. Dear me, woman, dinna let the loss of the world's gear bereave ye of your senses. I would rather make ye a present of a dozen mug-ewes of the Tinwald brood myself; and now I think on't, if ye'll send over Elphin, I will help him hame with them in the gloaming myself. So, Phemie, woman, be comforted.'

At the mention of her brother's name she cried out, 'Where is he? Oh, where is he?' gazed wildly round, and, shuddering from head to foot, fell senseless on the floor. Other inhabitants of the valley, alarmed by the sudden swell of the river, which had augmented to a torrent, deep and impassable, now came in to inquire if any loss had been sustained, for numbers of sheep and teds of hay had been observed floating down about the dawn of the morning.

They assisted in reclaiming the unhappy maiden from her swoon; but insensibility was joy compared to the sorrow to which she awakened. 'They have ta'en him away, they have ta'en him away,' she chanted, in a tone of delirious pathos; 'him that was whiter and fairer than the lily on Lyddal Lee. They have long sought and they have long sued, and they had the power to prevail against my prayers at last. They have ta'en him away; the flower is plucked from among the weeds, an the dove is slain amid a flock of ravens. They came withshout, and they came with song, and they spread the charm, and they placed the spell, and the baptised brow has been bowed down to the unbaptised hand. They have ta'en him away, they have ta'en him away; he was too lovely, and too good, and too noble, to bless us with his continuance on earth; for what are the sons of men compared to him? – the light of the moonbeam to the morning sun, the glow-worm to the eastern star. They have ta'en him away, the invisible dwellers of the earth. I saw them come on him with shouting and with singing, and they charmed him where he sat, and away they bore him; an the horse he rode was never shod with iron, nor owned before the mastery of human hand. They have ta'en him away over the water, and over the wood, and over the hill. I got but ae look of his bonnie blue ee, but ae, ae look. But as I have endured what never maiden endured, so will undertake what never maiden undertook; I will win him from them all. I know the invisible ones of the earth; I have heard their wild and wondrous music in the wild woods, and there shall a christened maiden seek him, and achieve his deliverance.' She paused, and glancing around a circle of condoling faces, down which the tears were dropping like rain, said, in a calm and altered but still delirious tone: 'Why do you weep, Mary Halliday? and why do you weep,

John Graeme? Ye think that Elphin Irving – oh, it's a bonnie, bonnie name, and dear to many a maiden's heart as well as mine – ye think he is drowned in Corrie, and ye will seek in the deep, deep pools for the bonnie, bonnie corse, that ye may weep over it, as it lies in its last linen, and lay it, amid weeping and wailing, in the dowie kirkyard. Ye may seek, but ye shall never find; so leave me to trim up my hair, and prepare my dwelling, and make myself ready to watch for the hour of his return to upper earth.' And she resumed her household labours with an alacrity which lessened not the sorrow of her friends.

Meanwhile the rumour flew over the vale that Elphin Irving was drowned in Corriewater. Matron and maid, old man and young, collected suddenly along the banks of the river, which now began to subside to its natural summer limits, and commenced their search; interrupted every now and then by calling from side to side, and from pool to pool, and by exclamations of sorrow for this misfortune. The search was fruitless: five sheep, pertaining to the flock which he conducted to pasture, were found drowned in one of the deep eddies; but the river was still too brown, from the soil of its moorland sources, to enable them to see what its deep shelves, its pools, and its overhanging and hazely banks concealed. They remitted further search till the stream should become pure; and old man taking old man aside, began to whisper about the mystery of the youth's disappearance; old women laid their lips to the ears of their coevals, and talked of Elphin Irving's fairy parentage, and . his having been dropped by an unearthly hand into a Christian cradle. The young men and maids conversed on other themes; they grieved for the loss of the friend and the lover, and while the former thought that a heart so kind and true was not left in the vale, the latter thought, as maidens will, on his handsome person, gentle manners, and merry blue eye, and speculated with a sigh on the time when they might have hoped a return for their love. They were soon joined by others who had heard the wild and delirious language of his sister: the old belief was added to the new assurance, and both again commented upon by minds full of superstitious feeling, and hearts full of supernatural fears, till the youths and maidens of Corrievale held no more love trystes for seven days and nights, lest, like Elphin Irving, they should be carried away to augment the ranks of the unchristened chivalry.

It was curious to listen to the speculations of the peasantry. 'For my part,' said a youth, 'if I were sure that poor Elphin escaped from that perilous water, I would not give the fairies a pound of hiplock wool for their chance of him. There has not been a fairy seen in the land since Donald Cargil, the Cameronian, conjured them into the Solway for playing on their pipes during one of his nocturnal preachings on the hip of the Burnswark hill.'

'Preserve me, bairn,' said an old woman, justly exasperated at the incredulity of her nephew, 'if ye winna believe what I both heard and saw at the moonlight end of Craigyburnwood on a summer night, rank after rank of the fairy folk, ye'll at least believe a douce man and a ghostly professor, even the late minister of Tinwaldkirk. His only son – I mind the lad weel, with his long yellow locks and his bonnie blue eyes – when I was but a gilpie of a lassie, *he* was stolen away from off the horse at his father's elbow, as they crossed that false and fearsome water, even Locherbriggflow, on the night of the Midsummer fair of Dumfries. Ay, ay – who can doubt the truth of that? Have not the godly inhabitants of Almsfieldtown and Tinwaldkirk seen the sweet youth riding at midnight, in the midst of the unhallowed troop, to the sound of flute and of dulcimer, and though meikle they prayed, naebody tried to achieve his deliverance?'

'I have heard it said by douce folk and sponsible,' interrupted another, 'that every seven years the elves and fairies pay kane,[1] or make an offering of one of their children, to the grand enemy of salvation, and that they are permitted to purloin one of the children of men to present to the fiend – a more acceptable offering, I'll warrant, than one of their own infernal brood that are Satan's sib allies, and drink a drop of the deil's blood every May morning. And touching this lost lad, ye all ken his mother was a hawk of an uncannie nest, a second cousin of Kate Kimmer, of Barfloshan, as rank a witch as ever rode on ragwort. Ay, sirs, what's bred in the bone is ill to come out of the flesh.'

On these and similar topics, which a peasantry full of ancient tradition and enthusiasm and superstition readily associate with the commonest occurrences of life, the people of Corrievale continued to converse till the fall of evening, when each, seeking their home, renewed again the wondrous subject, and illustrated it with all that popular belief and poetic imagination could so abundantly supply.

The night which followed this melancholy day was wild with wind and rain; the river came down broader and deeper than before, and the lightning, flashing by fits over the green woods of Corrie, showed the ungovernable and perilous flood sweeping above its banks. It happened that a farmer, returning from one of the Border fairs, encountered the full swing of the storm; but mounted on an excellent horse, and mantled from chin to heel in a good grey plaid, beneath which he had the further security of a thick greatcoat, he sat dry in his saddle, and proceeded in the

[1]Tribute paid in kind.

anticipated joy of a subsided tempest and a glowing morning sun. As he entered the long grove, or rather remains of the old Galwegian forest, which lines for some space the banks of the Corriewater, the storm began to abate, the wind sighed milder and milder among the trees and here and there a star, twinkling momentarily through the sudden rack of the clouds, showed the river raging from bank to brae. As he shook the moisture from his clothes, he was not without a wish that the day would dawn, and that he might be preserved on a road which his imagination beset with greater perils than the raging river; for his superstitious feeling let loose upon his path elf and goblin, and the current traditions of the district supplied very largely to his apprehension the ready materials of fear.

Just as he emerged from the wood, where a fine sloping bank, covered with short greensward, skirts the limit of the forest, his horse made a full pause, snorted, trembled, and started from side to side, stooped his head, erected his ears, and seemed to scrutinise every tree and bush. The rider, too, it may be imagined, gazed round and round, peered warily into every suspicious-looking place. His dread of a supernatural visitation was not much allayed when he observed a female shape seated on the ground at the root of a huge old oak-tree, which stood in the centre of one of those patches of verdant sward, known by the name of 'fairy-rings', and avoided by all peasants who wish to prosper. A long thin gleam of eastern daylight enabled him to examine accurately the being who, in this wild place and unusual hour, gave additional terror to this haunted spot. She was dressed in white from the neck to the knees; her arms, long and round and white, were perfectly bare; her head, uncovered, allowed her long hair to descend in ringlet succeeding ringlet, till the half of her person was nearly concealed in the fleece. Amidst the whole, her hands were constantly busy in shedding aside the tresses which interposed between her steady and uninterrupted gaze down a line of old road which winded among the hills to an ancient burial-ground.

As the traveller continued to gaze, the figure suddenly rose, and, wringing the rain from her long locks, paced round and round the tree, chanting in a wild and melancholy manner an equally wild and delirious song.

THE FAIRY OAK OF CORRIEWATER

The small bird's head is under its wing,
    The deer sleeps on the grass;
The moon comes out, and the stars shine down,
    The dew gleams like the glass:
There is no sound in the world so wide,
    Save the sound of the smitten brass,
With the merry cittern and the pipe
    Of the fairies as they pass.
But oh! the fire maun burn and burn,
And the hour is gone, and will never return.

The green hill cleaves, and forth, with a hound,
    Comes elf and elfin steed;
The moon dives down in a golden cloud,
    The stars grow dim with dread;
But a light is running along the earth,
    So of heaven's they have no need:
O'er moor and moss with a shout they pass,
    And the word is spur and speed –
But the fire maun burn, and I maun quake,
And the hour is gone that will never come back.

And when they came to Craigyburnwood,
   The Queen of the Fairies spoke:
'Come, bind your steeds to the rushes so green,
   And dance by the haunted oak:
I found the acorn on Heshbon Hill,
   In the nook of a palmer's poke,
A thousand years since; here it grows!'
   And they danced till the greenwood shook:
But oh! the fire, the burning fire,
The longer it burns, it but blazes the higher.

'I have won me a youth,' the Elf Queen said,
   'The fairest that earth may see;
This night I have won young Elph Irving
   My cupbearer to be.
His service lasts but for seven sweet years,
   And his wage is a kiss of me.'
And merrily, merrily, laughed the wild elves
   Round Corrie's greenwood tree.
But oh! the fire it glows in my brain,
And the hour is gone, and comes not again.

The Queen she has whispered a secret word,
   'Come hither, my Elphin sweet,
And bring that cup of the charméd wine,
   Thy lips and mine to weet.'
But a brown elf shouted a loud, loud shout,
   'Come, leap on your coursers fleet,
For here comes the smell of some baptised flesh,
   And the sounding of baptised feet.'
But oh! the fire that burns, and maun burn;
For the time that is gone will never return.

On a steed as white as the new-milked milk,
   The Elf Queen leaped with a bound,
And young Elphin a steed like December snow
   'Neath him at the word he found.
But a maiden came, and her christened arms
   She linked her brother around,
And called on God, and the steed with a snort
   Sank into the gaping ground.
But the fire maun burn, and I maun quake,
And the time that is gone will no more come back.

And she held her brother, and lo! he grew
   A wild bull waked in ire;
And she held her brother, and lo! he changed
   To a river roaring higher;
And she held her brother, and he became
   A flood of the raging fire;
She shrieked and sank, and the wild elves laughed
   Till the mountain rang and mire.
But oh! the fire yet burns in my brain,
And the hour is gone, and comes not again.

'O maiden, why waxed thy faith so faint,
   Thy spirit so slack and slaw?
Thy courage kept good till the flame waxed wud,[1]
   Then thy might began to thaw;
Had ye kissed him with thy christened lip,
   Ye had wan him frae 'mang us a'.
Now bless the fire, the elfin fire,
   That made thee faint and fa';
Now bless the fire, the elfin fire,
   The longer it burns it blazes the higher.'

[1]Furious.

At the close of this unusual strain the figure sat down on the grass, and proceeded to bind up her long and disordered tresses, gazing along the old and unfrequented road. 'Now God be my helper,' said the traveller, who happened to be the laird of Johnstone Bank, 'can this be a trick of the fiend, or can it be bonnie Phemie Irving who chants this dolorous sang? Something sad has befallen, that makes her seek her seat in this eerie nook amid the darkness and tempest: through might from aboon I will go on and see.' And the horse, feeling something of the owner's reviving spirit in the application of spur-steel, bore him at once to the foot of the tree. The poor delirious maiden uttered a yell of piercing joy as she beheld him, and, with the swiftness of a creature winged, linked her arms round the rider's waist, and shrieked till the woods rang. 'Oh, I have ye now, Elphin, I have ye now,' and she strained him to her bosom with a convulsive grasp. 'What ails ye, my bonnie lass?' said the laird of Johnstone Bank, his fears of the supernatural vanishing when he beheld her sad and bewildered look. She raised her eyes at the sound, and, seeing a strange face, her arms slipped their hold, and she dropped with a groan on the ground.

The morning had now fairly broke: the flocks shook the rain from their sides, the shepherds hastened to inspect their charges, and a thin blue smoke began to stream from the cottages of the valley into the brightening air. The laird carried Phemie Irving in his arms, till he observed two shepherds ascending from one of the loops of Corriewater, bearing the lifeless body of her brother. They had found him whirling round and round in one of the numerous eddies, and his hands, clutched and filled with wool, showed that he had lost his life in attempting to save the flock of his sister. A plaid was laid over the body, which, along with the unhappy maiden in a half-lifeless state, was carried into a cottage, and laid in that apartment distinguished among the peasantry by the name of the chamber. While the peasant's wife was left to take care of Phemie, old man and matron and maid had collected around the drowned youth, and each began to relate the circumstances of his death, when the door suddenly opened, and his sister, advancing to the corpse with a look of delirious serenity, broke out into a wild laugh and said: 'Oh, it is wonderful, it's truly wonderful! That bare and death-cold body, dragged from the darkest pool of Corrie, with its hands filled with fine wool, wears the perfect similitude of my own Elphin! I'll tell ye – the spiritual dwellers of the earth, the fairyfolk of our evening tale, have stolen the living body, and fashioned this cold and inanimate clod to mislead your pursuit. In common eyes this seems all that Elphin Irving would be, had he sunk in Corriewater; but so it seems not to me. Ye have sought the living soul, and ye have found only its garment. But oh, if ye had beheld him, as I beheld him tonight, riding among the elfin troop, the fairest of them all; had you clasped him in your arms, and wrestled for him with spirits and terrible shapes from the other world, till your heart quailed and your flesh was subdued, then would ye yield no credit to the semblance which this cold and apparent flesh bears to my brother. But hearken! On Hallowmass Eve, when the spiritual people are let loose on earth for a season, I will take my stand in the burial-ground of Corrie; and when my Elphin and his unchristened troop come past, with the sound of all their minstrelsy, I will leap on him and win him, or perish for ever.'

All gazed aghast on the delirious maiden, and many of her auditors gave more credence to her distempered speech than to the visible evidence before them. As she turned to depart, she looked round, and suddenly sunk upon the body, with tears streaming from her eyes, and sobbed out, 'My brother! oh, my brother!' She was carried out insensible, and again recovered; but relapsed into her ordinary delirium, in which she continued till the Hallow Eve after her brother's burial. She was found seated in the ancient burial-ground, her back against a broken gravestone, her locks white with frost-rime, watching with intensity of look the road to the kirkyard; but the spirit which gave life to the fairest form of all the maids of Annandale was fled for ever.

Such is the singular story which the peasants know by the name of 'Elphin Irving, the Fairies' Cupbearer'; and the title, in its fullest and most supernatural sense, still obtains credence among the industrious and virtuous dames of the romantic vale of Corrie.

COUSIN MATTIE*

At the lone farm of Finagle, there lived for many years an industrious farmer and his family. Several of his children died, and only one daughter and one son remained to him. He had besides these a little orphan niece, who was brought into the family, called Matilda; but all her days she went by the familiar name of Cousin Mattie. At the time this simple narrative commences, Alexander, the farmer's son, was six years of age, Mattie was seven, and Flora, the farmer's only daughter, about twelve.

How I do love a little girl about that age! There is nothing in nature so fascinating, so lovely, so innocent; and, at the same time, so full of gaiety and playfulness. The

*James Hogg, *The Ettrick Shepherd's Tales*.

tender and delicate affections, to which their natures are moulded, are then beginning unconsciously to form; and everything beautiful or affecting in nature claims from them a deep but momentary interest. They have a tear for the weaned lamb, for the drooping flower, and even for the travelling mendicant, though afraid to come near him. But the child of the poor female vagrant is to them, of all others, an object of the deepest interest. How I have seen them look at the little wretch, and then at their own parents alternately, the feelings of the soul abundantly conspicuous in every muscle of the face and turn of the eye! Their hearts are like softened wax, and the impressions then made on them remain for ever. Such beings approach nigh to the list where angels stand, and are, in fact, the connecting link that joins us with the inhabitants of a better world. How I do love a well-educated little girl of twelve or thirteen years of age!

At such an age was Flora of Finagle, with a heart moulded to every tender impression, and a memory so retentive that whatever affected or interested her was engraven there never to be cancelled.

One morning, after her mother had risen and gone to the byre to look after the cows, Flora, who was lying in a bed by herself, heard the following dialogue between the two children, who were lying prattling together in another bed close beside hers –

'Do you ever dream ony, little Sandy?'

'What is't like, cousin Mattie? Sandy no ken what it is til deam.'

'It is to think ye do things when you are sleeping, when ye dinna do them at a'.'

'Oh, Sandy deam a great deal yat way.'

'If you will tell me ane o' your dreams, Sandy – I'll tell

you ane o' mine that I dreamed last night; and it was about you, Sandy?'

'Sae was mine, cousin. Sandy deamed that he fightit a gaet Englishman, an' it was Yobin Hood; an' Sandy ding'd him's swold out o' him's hand, an' noll'd him on ye face, an' ye back, till him geetit. An' yen thele comed anodel littel despelyate Englishman, an' it was littel John; an' Sandy fightit him till him was dead; an' yen Sandy got on o' ane gyand holse, an' gallompit away.'

'But I wish that ye be nae making that dream just e'en now, Sandy?'

'Sandy 'hought it, atweel.'

'But were you sleeping when you thought it?'

'Na, Sandy wasna' sleepin', but him was winking.'

'Oh, but that's not a true dream; I'll tell you one that's a true dream. I thought there was a bonny lady came to me, and she held out two roses, a red one and a pale one, and bade me take my choice. I took the white one; and she bade me keep it, and never part with it, for if I gave it away, I would die. But when I came to you, you asked my rose, and I refused to give you it. You then cried for it, and said I did not love you; so I could not refuse you the flower, but wept too, and you took it.

'Then the bonny lady came back to me, and was very angry, and said, "Did not I tell you to keep your rose? Now the boy that you have given it to will be your murderer. He will kill you; and on this day fortnight you will be lying in your coffin, and that pale rose upon your breast."

'I said, "I could not help it now." But when I was told that you were to kill me, I liked you aye better and better, and better and better.' And with these words Matilda clasped him to her bosom and wept. Sandy sobbed bitterly too, and said, 'She be geat lial, yon lady. Sandy no kill cousin Mattie. When Sandy gows byaw man, an' gets a gyand house, him be vely good till cousin an' feed hel wi' gingebead, an' yeam, an' tyankil, an' take hel in him's bosy yis way.' With that the two children fell silent, and sobbed and wept till they fell sound asleep, clasped in each other's arms.

This artless dialogue made a deep impression on Flora's sensitive heart. It was a part of her mother's creed to rely on dreams, so that it had naturally become Flora's too. She was shocked, and absolutely terrified, when she heard her little ingenious cousin say that Sandy was to murder her, and on that day fortnight she should be lying in her coffin; and without informing her mother of what she had over-heard, she resolved in her own mind to avert, if possible, the impending evil. It was on a Sabbath morning, and after little Sandy had got on his clothes, and while Matilda was out, he attempted to tell his mother cousin Mattie's dream, to Flora's great vexation; but he made such a blundering story of it that it proved altogether incoherent, and his mother took no further notice of it than to bid him hold his tongue; 'what was that he was speaking about murdering?'

The next week Flora entreated of her mother that she would suffer cousin Mattie and herself to pay a visit to their aunt at Kirkmichael; and, though her mother was unwilling, she urged her suit so earnestly that the worthy dame was fain to consent.

'What's ta'en the gowk[1] lassie the day?' said she; 'I think she be gane fey. I never could get her to gang to see her aunt, and now she has ta'en a tirrovy[2] in her head, that she'll no be keepit. I dinna like sic absolute freaks, an' sic

[1] Foolish.
[2] Fit of passion.

langings, to come into the heads o' bairns; they're ower aften afore something uncannie. Gae your ways an' see your auntie, sin' ye will gang; but ye's no get little cousin w'ye, sae never speak o't. Think ye that I can do wantin' ye baith out o' the house till the Sabbath day be ower.'

'Oh but, mother, it's sae gousty,[1] an' sae eiry, to lie up in yon loft ane's lane; unless cousin Mattie gang wi' me, I canna' gang ava.'

'Then just stay at hame, daughter, an' let us alane o' thae daft nories[2] a' thegither.'

Flora now had recourse to that expedient which never fails to conquer the opposition of a fond mother: she pretended to cry bitterly. The good dame was quite overcome, and at once yielded, though not with a very good grace. 'Saw ever onybody sic a fie-gae-to[3] as this? They that will to Cupar maun to Cupar! Gae your ways to Kirkmichael, an' tak the hale town at your tail, gin ye like. What's this that I'm sped wi'.'

'Na, na, mother; I's no gang my foot length. Ye sanna hae that to flyre[4] about. Ye keep me working frae the tae year's end to the tither, an' winna gie me a day to mysel'. I's no seek to be away again, as lang as I'm aneath your roof.'

'Whisht now, an' haud your tongue, my bonny Flora. Ye hae been ower good a bairn to me, no to get your ain way o' ten times mair nor that. Ye ken laith wad your mother be to contrair you i' ought, if she wist it war for your good. I'm right glad that it has come i' your ain side o' the house, to gang an' see your auntie. Gang your ways, an' stay a day

[1]Ghostly.
[2]Whims.
[3]Ado.
[4]Complain.

or twa; an', if ye dinna like to sleep your lane, take billy Sandy w'ye, an' leave little cousin wi' me, to help me wi' bits o' turns till ye come back.'

This arrangement suiting Flora's intent equally well with the other, it was readily agreed to, and everything soon amicably settled between the mother and daughter. The former demurred a little on Sandy's inability to perform the journey; but Flora, being intent on her purpose, overruled this objection, though she knew it was but too well founded.

Accordingly, the couple set out on their journey next morning, but before they were half way Sandy began to tire, and a short time after gave fairly in. Flora carried him on her back for a space, but finding that would never do, she tried to cajole him into further exertion. No, Sandy would not set a foot to the ground. He was grown drowsy, and would not move. Flora knew not what to do, but at length fell upon an expedient which an older person would scarcely have thought of. She went to a gate of an enclosure, and, pulling a spoke out of it, she brought that to Sandy, telling him she had now got him a fine horse, and he might ride all the way. Sandy, who was uncommonly fond of horses, swallowed the bait, and, mounting astride on his rung, he took the road at a round pace, and for the last two miles of their journey Flora could hardly keep in view of him.

She had little pleasure in her visit, further than the satisfaction that she was doing what she could to avert a dreadful casualty, which she dreaded to be hanging over the family; and on her return, from the time that she came in view of her father, she looked only for the appearance of Mattie running about the door; but no Mattie being seen, Flora's heart began to tremble, and as she advanced nearer, her knees grew so feeble that they would scarcely support her slender form; for she knew that it was one of the radical principles of a dream to be ambiguous.

'A's unco still about our hame the day, Sandy; I wish ilka ane there may be weel. It's like death.'

'Sandy no ken what death *is* like. What *is* it like, Sistel Flola?'

'You will maybe see that ower soon. It is death that kills a' living things, Sandy.'

'Aye; aih aye! Sandy saw a wee buldie, it could neilel pick, nol flee, nol dab. It was vely ill done o' death! Sistel Flola, didna God make a' living things?'

'Yes; be assured he did.'

'Then, what has death ado to kill them? if Sandy wele God, him wad fight him.'

'Whisht, whisht, my dear; ye dinna ken what you're sayin'. Ye maunna speak about these things.'

'Weel, Sandy no speak ony maile about them. But if death should kill cousin Mattie, oh! Sandy wish him might kill him too!'

'Wha do ye like best i' this world, Sandy?'

'Sandy like sistel Flola best.'

'You are learning the art of flattery already; for I heard ye telling Mattie the tither morning, that ye likit her better than a' the rest o' the world put thegither.'

'But yan Sandy coudna help yat. Cousin Mattie like Sandy, and what could him say?'

Flora could not answer him for anxiety; for they were now drawing quite near to the house, and still all was quiet. At length Mattie opened the door, and, without returning to tell her aunt the joyful tidings, came running like a little fairy to meet them; gave Flora a hasty kiss; and then, clasping little Sandy about the neck, she exclaimed, in an ecstatic tone, 'Aih, Sandy man!' and pressed her cheek to his. Sandy produced a small book of pictures, and a pink rose knot that he had brought for his cousin, and was repaid with another embrace, and a sly compliment to his gallantry.

Matilda was far beyond her years in acuteness. Her mother was an accomplished English lady, though only the daughter of a poor curate, and she had bred her only child with every possible attention. She could read, she could sing, and play some airs on the spinnet; and was altogether a most interesting little nymph. Both her parents came to an untimely end, and to the lone cottage of Finagle was she then removed, where she was still very much caressed. She told Flora all the news of her absence in a breath. There was nothing disastrous had happened. But, so strong was Flora's presentiment of evil, that she could not get quit of it, until she had pressed the hands of both her parents. From that day forth, she suspected that little faith was to be put in dreams. The fourteen days was now fairly over, and no evil nor danger had happened to Matilda, either from the hand of Sandy or otherwise. However, she kept the secret of the dream locked up in her heart, and never either mentioned or forgot it.

Shortly after that she endeavoured to reason her mother out of her belief in dreams, for she would still gladly have been persuaded in her own mind that this vision was futile, and of no avail. But she found her mother staunch to her point. She reasoned on the principle that the Almighty had made nothing in vain, and if dreams had been of no import to man they would not have been given to him. And further, she said we read in the Scriptures that dreams were fulfilled in the days of old; but we didna read in the Scriptures that ever the nature of dreaming was changed.

On the contrary, she believed that since the days of prophecy had departed, and no more warnings of futurity could be derived by man from that, dreaming was of doubly more avail, and ought to be proportionally more attended to, as the only mystical communication remaining between God and man. To this reasoning Flora was obliged to yield. It is no hard matter to conquer, where belief succeeds argument.

Time flew on, and the two children were never asunder. They read together, prayed together, and toyed and caressed without restraint, seeming but to live for one another. But a heavy misfortune at length befell the family. She who had been a kind mother and guardian angel to all the three was removed by death to a better home. Flora was at that time in her eighteenth year, and the charge of the family then devolved on her. Great was their grief, but their happiness was nothing abated; they lived together in the same kind love and amity as they had done before. The two youngest in particular fondled each other more and more, and this growing fondness, instead of being checked, was constantly encouraged, Flora still having a lurking dread that some deadly animosity might breed between them.

Matilda and she always slept in the same bed, and very regularly told each other their dreams in the morning – dreams pure and innocent as their own stainless bosoms. But one morning Flora was surprised by Matilda addressing her as follows, in a tone of great perplexity and distress –

'Ah! my dear cousin, what a dream I have had last night! I thought I saw my aunt, your late worthy mother, who was kind and affectionate to me, as she always wont to be, and more beautiful than I ever saw her. She took me in her arms, and wept over me; and charged me to go and leave this place instantly, and by all means to avoid her son, otherwise he was destined to be my murderer and on that day seven-night I should be lying in my coffin. She showed me a sight too that I did not know, and cannot give a name to. But the surgeons came between us, and separated us, so that I saw her no more."

Flora trembled and groaned in spirit; nor could she make any answer to Matilda for a long space, save repeated moans. 'Merciful Heaven!' said she at length, 'what can such a dream portend? Do not you remember, dear Mattie, of dreaming a dream of the same nature once long ago?'

Mattie had quite forgot of ever having dreamed such a dream; but Flora remembered it well; and thinking that she might formerly have been the mean, under Heaven, of counterworking destiny, she determined to make a further effort; and, ere ever she arose, advised Matilda to leave the house, and avoid her brother, until the seven days had elapsed. 'It can do nae ill, Mattie,' said she; 'an' mankind hae whiles muckle i' their ain hands to do or no to do; to bring about, or to keep back.' Mattie consented, solely to please the amiable Flora; for she was no more afraid of Sandy than she was of one of the flowers of the field. She went to Kirkmichael, stayed till the week was expired, came home in safety, and they both laughed at their superstitious fears. Matilda thought of the dream no more; but Flora treasured it up in her memory, though all the coincidence that she could discover between the two dreams was that they had both happened on a Saturday, and both precisely at the same season of the year, which she well remembered.

At the age of two and twenty, Flora was married to a young farmer, who lived in a distant corner of the same extensive parish; and of course left the charge of her father's household to cousin Mattie, who, with the old farmer, his son, and one maid-servant, managed and did all the work of the farm. Still, as their number was diminished, their affections seemed to be drawn the closer; but Flora scarcely saw them any more, having the concerns of a family to mind at home.

One day, when her husband went to church, he perceived the old beadle standing bent over his staff at the churchyard gate, distributing burial letters to a few as they entered. He held out one to the husband of Flora, and, at the same time, touched the front of his bonnet with the other hand; and without regarding how the letter affected him who received it, began instantly to look about for others to whom he had letters directed.

The farmer opened the letter, and had almost sunk down on the earth, when he read as follows:

'Sir, The favour of your company, at twelve o'clock, on Tuesday next, to attend the funeral of Matilda A——n, my niece, from this, to the place of interment, in the church yard of C——r, will much oblige, Sir, your humble servant,

'JAMES A——N.

'Finagle, April 12th.'

Think of Flora's amazement and distress, when her husband told her what had happened, and showed her this letter. She took to her bed on the instant, and wept herself into a fever for the friend and companion of her youth. Her husband became considerably alarmed on her account, she being in that state in which violent excitement often proves dangerous. Her sickness was, however, only temporary; but she burned with impatience to learn some particulars of her cousin's death. Her husband could tell her nothing; only, that he heard one say *she died on Saturday*.

This set Flora a calculating, and going over in her mind reminiscences of their youth; and she soon discovered, to her utter astonishment and even horror, that her cousin Matilda had died precisely on *that day fourteen years* that she first dreamed the ominous dream, and that day seven years that she dreamed it again!

Here was indeed matter of wonder! But her blood ran cold to her heart when she thought what might have been the manner of her death. She dreaded, nay, she almost calculated upon it as certain, that her brother had poisoned, or otherwise made away privately with the deceased, as she was sure such an extraordinary coincidence behoved to be fulfilled in all its parts. She durst no more make any inquiries concerning the circumstances of her cousin's death; but she became moping and unsettled, and her husband feared for her reason.

He went to the funeral; but dreading to leave Flora long by herself, he only met the procession a small space from the churchyard; for his father-in-law's house was distant fourteen miles from his own. On his return, he could still give Flora very little additional information. He said he had asked his father-in-law what had been the nature of the complaint of which she died; but he had given him an equivocal answer, and seemed to avoid entering into any explanation; and that he had then made inquiry at others, who all testified their ignorance of the matter. Flora at length, after long hesitation, ventured to ask *if her brother was at the funeral?* and was told that he was not. This was a death-blow to her lingering hopes, and all but confirmed the hideous catastrophe that she dreaded; and for the remainder of that week she continued in a state of mental agony.

On the Sunday following, she manifested a strong desire to go to church to visit her cousin's grave. Her husband opposed it at first, but at last consenting, in hopes she might be benefited by an overflow of tenderness, he mounted her on a pad, and accompanied her to the church-yard gate, leaving her there to give vent to her feelings.

As she approached the new grave, which was by the side of her mother's, she perceived two aged people whom she knew, sitting beside it busily engaged in conversation about the inhabitant below. Flora drew her hood over her face, and came with a sauntering step towards them, to lull all suspicion that she had any interest or concern in what they were saying; and finally she leaned herself down on a flat grave-stone close beside them, and made as if she were busied in deciphering the inscription. There she heard the following dialogue, one may conceive with what sort of feelings.

'An' then she was aye sae kind, an' sae lively, an' sae affable to poor an' rich, an' then sae bonny an' sae young. Oh, but my heart's sair for her! When I saw the mortcláith drawn off the coffin, an' saw the silver letters kythe, AGED 21, the tears ran down ower thae auld wizzened cheeks, Janet; an' I said to mysel', "Wow but that is a bonny flower cut off i' the bloom!" But, Janet, my joe, warna ye at the corps-kisting.'[1]

'An' what suppose I was, Matthew? What's your concern wi' that?'

'Because I heard say that there was nane there but you an' another that ye ken weel. But canna you tell me, kimmer, what was the corpse like? Was't a' fair an' bonny, an' nae blueness nor demmish to be seen?'

'An' what wad an auld fool body like you be the better, gin ye kend what the corpse was like? Thae sights are nae for een like yours to see; an' thae subjects are nae fit for tongues like yours to tattle about: What's done canna be

[1] Ceremony of coffining.

undone. The dead will lie still. But oh, what's to come o' the living?'

'Ay, but I'm sure she had been a lusty weel plenish corpse, Janet; for she was a heavy ane; an' a deeper coffin I never saw.'

'Haud your auld souple untackit tongue. Gin I hear sic another hint come ower the foul tap o't, it sal be the waur for ye. But lown be it spoken, an' little be it said. Weel might the corpse be heavy, an' the coffin deep! ay, weel might the coffin be made deep, Matthew, for there was a stout lad bairn, a poor little pale flower, that hardly ever saw the light o' heaven, was streekit[1] on her breast at the same time wi' hersel'.'

RAT HALL*

'Rats leaving their usual haunts in your houses, barns, and stackyards, and going to the fields, is an unfortunate omen for the person whose abode they leave.' So wrote one Wilkie, author of a manuscript collection of old Border customs and superstitions, compiled, in the commencement of the present century, for the use of Sir Walter Scott. The following incident illustrating the belief is related as having occurred upon the estate of the present writer. In the early years of the present century, the farm of Maisondieu was tenanted by a family named Fortune, who had been for several generations in occupation, and were reputed to have held land in the neighbourhood for above two hundred years. The name Maisondieu, it may be stated in passing, was derived from a religious house, or hospital, 'for the

[1] Laid out.
*The Editor, *The New Border Tales*.

reception of pilgrims, the diseased, and the indigent', which had formerly stood upon the present farm lands.

At last a crisis in the history of the Fortune family arrived. The old farmer died, leaving a son of some three or four and twenty years of age to succeed him. Robert Fortune, the younger, was a fine young man, who lacked not spirit or ability so much as principle and steadiness. Left to his own devices, with money in his pocket, and without guide, monitor, or controller, he seemed to have set himself to dissipate alike the reputation and the fortune which had been acquired through the prudence and good conduct of his forebears. He had enrolled himself a member of a local corps of Yeomanry Cavalry, which had been raised in the expectation of a French Invasion; and he was bent upon cutting a dash. He prided himself upon the horses he rode; and many were the scenes of midnight carousal, and of hare-brained prank and horse-play, enacted by himself and his hot-blooded, would-be fire-eating companions in the old farm-house at this period. For a brief time things went as merrily as the marriage bell of the proverb; but then a change set in. Peace was proclaimed, and farmers' prices, which the war had kept high, fell. A succession of bad seasons followed; and, instead of meeting them by retrenchment, young Fortune turned for consolation in the troubles which they brought him to a still more reckless extravagance. His elders shook their heads, and people began to say, when his back was turned, that he was going to the dogs. In time, the pinch of poverty began to be felt at Maisondieu. The Yeomanry had been disbanded, and Robert now sat alone by his black hearth. To drive out the cold, and raise his spirits to the pitch which they had known in happy bygone days, he resorted to the bottle. This, of course, made matters worse.

He neglected his business, his accounts were not kept, and his affairs became disordered. The house fell into a state of disrepair, which, being allowed to continue, grew rapidly worse; and the servants, observing their master's weakness, ceased to respect him, and at last, being gained upon by a feeling that he was a man who was going fast down the hill, took to scamping their work or shirking it.

But, if he found himself deserted by his boon companions – friends of a summer day – a new set of associates began to gather in force about poor Bob. If, instead of describing him as going 'to the dogs', people had said to the 'rats', it would have been more literally correct. Only it was the rats who came to him. They had long infested the farmyard; and now, in the general relaxing of former strictness, they had succeeded in effecting an entrance into the house. And, having once entered, they held the advantage they had gained. At first their presence was only made known at night, after the lights had been put out, and the inmates of the house had withdrawn to bed. Then, indeed, they held high revels in the kitchen – as a continual sound of skurrying feet, the occasional whisking of a tail upon the wainscot, the overturning with a clatter or a crash of some vessel of tin or earthenware, or the bold bounding of some more than commonly intrepid adventurer, allowed all men to be aware. So long, they were heard, and their devastations were felt; but the devastators were not seen. But, in course of time, finding themselves masters of the situation, they grew bolder, and ventured abroad by daylight too. Then it came to be no uncommon sight to see a rat cross the passage in front of you; or, on entering the kitchen, to catch sight of one suspended by his fore-feet, his tail depending behind him, sampling the contents of some butter-jar, or dripping-pot, which had been left unlidded on the table.

When he saw himself detected, the rat would beat a leisurely retreat; and there was insolence in his carriage and in the sweep of his tail, as though he knew his adversary's weakness. It was observed at this time that though the farmer, his man, and maid, grew lean, the rats on the farm grew fat. At last, with high living and impunity, their boldness grew beyond all bounds, and from the kitchen they extended their playground so as to comprise the whole house. Then it became a common occurrence for a rat to run across you whilst you lay in bed; or, if your toes peeped out at the foot of a short coverlet, for you to feel one nibbling at them. Or a rat might even hang feeding on the draught-blown, guttering candle at the farmer's very elbow, whilst he himself sat late into the night, plunged in a heavy reverie, the result, in equal parts, of his troubles and his potations. So is it with a certain class of humanity, who feed and flourish amid the misfortune and the decline of their betters. The depredations committed were enormous; for when they could not spoil or devour food or other property, the rats would carry it away. No contrivance was of the smallest use against them, for they soon understood the nature of the most ingenious trap, whilst poison failed to tempt them. Thus, whilst increasing in size, they increased so amazingly in numbers that – its owner being by this time so down in the world as to appear a safe butt for insolence – the old and formerly much respected house of Maisondieu now received from the profane the nickname of 'Rat Hall'.

It was about this time that the remarkable incident with which my story is concerned was witnessed by an old shepherd in Fortune's service. The family of Hall, a race of shepherds, had been long associated with that of Fortune upon the farm of Maisondieu; and old Bauldy, its present repre-

sentative, was now, in his own phrase, 'the fourth generation serving the fourth generation'. Greatly older and by
nature more thoughtful than his master, he, of course,
viewed the state of matters on the farm with a heavy heart,
and looked forward with the gloomiest forebodings to the
time when, as it seemed, he must inevitably be separated
from that master, whom, in spite of faults, he loved, and
from the spot where he had spent a long and happy life-
time. Well, one night in spring-time, he was sadly returning
to the onstead after a visit to his lambs. A brilliant moon
rode in a clear sky, and as he skirted an old hedge which
separates the farm premises from a field, at that time in
grass, he saw before him a single rat.

'Bad luck to you!' he murmured, under his breath, 'for ye
have brought bad luck on us.'

The rat, which had come out of a rat-hole in the bank
(which was perfectly riddled with them), now seemed to
look about him. The shepherd watched it. Returning to the
hole, it re-appeared, accompanied by a second rat. They in
turn looked about them, and perhaps compared notes as to
what they saw, for this time one only retired to the hole. It
was absent during some moments, and then returned,
bringing with it a very large old rat, which it piloted with
care. The hair upon the face of the old rat was white with
age; and the shepherd observed that it was blind. His
interest was by this time thoroughly aroused, and grasping
his tall crook with both hands, he rested his cheek against
his arms and watched, intently and in silence, from the
black shadow of the hedge. And now he witnessed what
amazed him. From each of the innumerable rat-holes in the
hedge-row, as if by magic, as if from a child's toy, there had
started forth a rat, which crouched, motionless and
listening, before the entrance to its cave. Their number, and

the uniformity of their action, gave to the effect presented the dignity of impressiveness. It was quite clear that they were acting, not by chance, but in the prosecution of some well-thought-out plan, upon some preconcerted signal.

As he watched them, Old Bauldy scarce drew his breath. The night was still; and when they had apparently satisfied themselves that the coast was clear, the rats advanced a little way. And as, in doing so, they brought their tails and hindquarters clear of the mouths of the rat-holes, they disclosed the nozzles and bright head-like eyes of other rats behind them. If it had been curiosity which had at first kept the shepherd motionless, it was the instinct of self-preservation which did so now. An army of rats such as he now beheld might well inspire uneasiness, nay, terror, in a braver man; and, as he gazed, its numbers were being every moment reinforced. For now, above the living silence of a country landscape contemplated by night, a low, but ever gathering and growing rumour was gradually making itself heard. It came from underground; and it was produced by the beating of many thousands of little feet upon the trodden earth of the runs. And, at last, whilst the sound increased in volume, by a hundred mouths the earth began to disgorge its living burthen. Rats! They were of the Norway breed, and first in order came the great males. These are used to live alone; if hunger presses them, they will prey on their own brood; they justly inspire terror. The less formidable females followed, each accompanied by her young. And ever as they swarmed in momentarily increasing numbers, as in the remote historical or mythical Migration of the Nations, the rear rank pushed the front rank before it, till the rats spread far afield, and the very ground seemed alive and moving with their multitudes. Transfixed in the attitude which he had at first assumed, the shepherd watched the spectacle – standing like a man who has been turned to stone, whom no earthly power could have induced to stir a finger. To say that never in his life before had he seen so many rats would be to utter idlest words. In no agonised vision of the night, lying stretched upon his pallet of chaff, whilst his breath froze, and his enemies disported themselves triumphantly, insultingly, upon the bare boards of the loft, peeped in on by a mischievous moon, had he ever *dreamed* of so many!

As has been said, during all this time it had been amply apparent that the rats were not acting without some plan of their own. Instead of following each one his own bent, they moved with the regularity and the discipline of trained forces manoeuvring in order. Nothing could have less resembled the blind infatuation of their fellows and predecessors, who had frisked at the heels of the Pied Piper through the streets of Hamelin to their doom. They had far more in common with the grim determination of the instruments of vengeance against Bishop Hatto. But their demeanour, if a little stern, was calm as well as resolute, as, inspired by a single purpose, controlled by a single will, they advanced, marching shoulder to shoulder. There were few stragglers, few weak places in their ranks. Their *morale* was very nearly perfect.

And now, when they had wheeled into the field, a touching incident occurred. The old hoary-faced rat had undoubtedly in his youth been marked by nature for a leader. But times were changed; he was old and blind, and for a moment he stood helpless before his people. For a moment, but no longer. Grasping the position of affairs, the rat who had been the first to appear, stepped forward to the rescue, and saved the situation. In his mouth he was observed to hold, by one of its ends, a straw – the other end of which he now dextrously inserted betwixt the jaws of the Patriarch, so as to form a sort of leading-string. And, thus coupled, the two rats moved off, and were followed by their thousands – the old rat, through the graceful intervention of the young one, still preserving every tittle of his dignity as a king and father of his people in this momentous crisis of his reign.

The shepherd watched the moving mass, as it passed across the moonlit surface of the field, like the shadow of a cloud, until at last it was lost to sight beyond a rising ground.

Then, and not till then, did he stir. Pulling himself hastily together, he made for the farm-house, and with the freedom which is allowed to an old servant, burst into his master's room. Fortune was seated at the table, his face buried in his hands. A sheet of printed paper lay before him.

'Bob! Bob!' cried the old man, 'we are presairved – the rats are gone!'

But Bob only lifted a heavy head and pointed, without speaking, to the paper which lay before him. It was an announcement that a 'displenishing sale' would shortly be held at Maisondieu.

'Lord! and has it come to this?'

'It has, indeed! I had not the heart to break it to you before, Bauldy.' And then he added with bitterness, 'We must have the usual jollification, I suppose. Well, there will be meat for many to provide that day; but I doubt 'twill be the poison of one.'

And so, sure enough, ere the Whitsuntide term-day arrived, the furniture and fittings of Maisondieu farm had fallen to the auctioneer's hammer; and Robert Fortune and his old and faithful shepherd had gone forth homeless, and in opposed directions, to face and fight the world.

It only remains to add that this story, wild as it may appear, is, in its main facts, currently related at the present day among the country-people of Roxburghshire.

NOTES TO 'ASSIPATTLE AND THE
MESTER STOORWORM'

BY MR. W. TRAILL DENNISON

[1]Assipattle was formerly used by Orcadians, in a kind of good-humoured derision, as a name for the youngest son. The writer, who happens to be a youngest son, was, when displaying any fit of youthful arrogance, often dubbed Assipattle by his elder brothers. They little knew that the term used as opprobrious fired in his mind the fond, vain hope of doing some great heroic deed, as Assipattle in the tales always did. The name and exploits of Assipattle were heard in many an Orkney fireside tale half a century ago. He is always represented as the youngest son, held in utter contempt by his elder brothers, and merely tolerated by his parents. He is the butt of all jokes, sometimes of blows and kicks. He lies in the ashes – from which he gets the first part of his name, *Assi* – and there moves hands and feet to and fro in lazy fashion, for the mere love of muscular motion. This motion gives rise to the latter part of his name, *pattle*. Some great emergency arises: a princess has to be delivered from some position of awful danger, or from the cave of some malignant trow; the corn and cattle have to be saved from the trows; or, as in our text, the land has to be delivered from the Stoorworm; and when all have failed to work deliverance, Assipattle rises to the occasion, and executes the daring deed that frees the land or the lady; he is covered with honour, and generally becomes the king's son-in-law. Indeed, Assipattle always begins in the deepest state of degradation, and ends on the highest summit of earthly glory. The idea is a fine antithesis, once highly appreciated by an unlettered peasantry. And I have, when a boy, heard many versions of this tale related by Orkney peasants. They are truly the oral and fireside heritage of the North.

Sir George Dasent, in presenting Assipattle in English garb, has given him the English name of Boots. I wish the learned gentleman could have seen the indignation of an old Orkney wife when I told her the name he had given Assipattle. She said, 'It was a sheem tae ca' Assipattle by sic a filthy neem. Bit what can ye lippen o' college-bred men? Deil a thing ken they bit college lair.' After giving the name by which our hero was known in different nations, Dasent says, 'The meaning of the word is, one who pokes about the ashes and blows up the fire; one who does dirty work,' etc. With us *Ass,* of course, means ashes. *Pattle* has here a different shade of meaning from poke. The Orkney word for poke is *purr*; and pattle is intended to convey a more lateral motion than poke. For example, if a fish is partly stranded in a shallow pool, in struggling to use tail and fins, the fish is said to *pattle* in the water. Our Assipattle did not sit poking, but lay grovelling, in the ashes.

[2]The Mester Stoorworm is the greatest of the great sea-serpents. Mester, that is master, as a prefix in our old tales, always means superior – it may be in strength, courage, cunning, or wisdom. Satan, for example, is the Master Deevil. Stoor, in Scotch, sometimes store, means large, powerful, strong, stern. Worm is a word applied in olden times to any animal of serpentine shape, irrespective of size. This use of the word worm is by no means confined to these islands.

Many other wild tales were at one time told about Stoorworms; but none of those creatures produced such tremendous effects, nor were of such gigantic size, as their parent, the Mester Stoorworm. Yet one of his offspring is represented as lying with one end off the North Cape, while the other end reached off Iceland. The very name is now almost obsolete here. It was first changed into Leviathan, derived from Scripture; and the newspapers have now made 'sea-serpent' a household word.

[3]*Rivlins*. A kind of sandal, made of rough cow-hide with the hair cut short, and worn with the hairy side out; they are still occasionally used in Orkney.

[4]*Thing*. The Great Council, or parliament, among the Norsemen.

[5]*Bokie*. A word representing any imaginary thing used to frighten children; a scarecrow. Scotch, bogle; English, bugbear.

[6]*Lawman*. President of the Thing.

[7]*Kemperman*. Probably fighting-man – one who fought in single combats, or competed at games, when required to do so by his master, who laid a stake on his success. The name was still used through Orkney during the last bygone century. Orkney lairds,

when making trading voyages, carried with them a Kemperman. He acted as footman to his master, by whom he was treated as an equal, and whose confidential adviser he often became.

[8]*Sickersnapper.* Probably 'severe biter'. Sicker, in the Orkney dialect, means severe; not secure, as in Scotch.

[9]*Oddie.* Is Odin here meant? The name Oddie is still used as a surname in Orkney.

[10]*Back of the lamp.* The back of the old Orkney lamp cast a dark shadow, so that by turning the suspended lamp on its swivel the shadow could be cast on any part of the room. Those wishing to avoid observation preferred to sit in this shadow.

[11]*Her.* There was no neuter gender in the Orkney dialect.

[12]*Ammers*, embers. *Wus*, was. *Unfeerdie*, unwieldy, unable. *Duff*, blunt – 'A duff edge cut slow'. *Wald*, wield. *Slockid*, extinguished.

[13]*Teetgong*, swift-go.

[14]*Sturtened*, congealed.

[15]*Meeracles*, phosphorescence of the sea.

[16]*Euse*, a large and very hot fire. The *e* is prefixed to give the word the sound of the German modified *u*.

[17]*Harskit*, heart-burn.

[18]*Rifts*, belches.

[19]*Travellye*, a sudden and violent fall.

[20]*Two bays.* Here came a long digression about a chart shown by a Captain Hewison to one of my narrator's ancestors, on which he saw the identical bays. Of course the Gulfs of Finland and Bothnia are meant.

[21]*Halflin*, a hobbledehoy.

[22]*Menye-singers*, men employed to sing on festive occasions.

[23]*Owercome*, the chorus of a song.

[24]*He.* Stones were always of the masculine gender.

[25]Many of our old tales conclude with this sentence. In our old dialect it ran thus: 'An' gin no' deed, dei'r livin' yet.'